Rebecca Sitton's

Spelling Sourcebook™
REVIEWS

Your Source for Blackline Master

Cloze Activities and

Dictation Sentences

for the High-Use

Writing Words 1–400

ISBN 1-886050-09-0
©1996—Rebecca Sitton
Egger Publishing, Inc.
P.O. Box 12248, Scottsdale, AZ 85267
Phone: 888-WE-SPELL (888-937-7355)
FAX: 480-951-2276

Rebecca Sitton's
SPELLING SOURCEBOOK™ SERIES

SOURCEBOOKS

- **"How-To" and "Why"**
  Your source for developing research-based spelling instruction for the writing-rich classroom.
  Sourcebook 1 Necessary for teachers in all grades.

- **Activities**
  Your source for skill-based activities for teaching and extending the high-use writing words.
  Sourcebook 2 Words 1–400 (grades 1–4)
  Sourcebook 3 Words 401–800 (grades 5–6)
  Sourcebook 4 Words 801–1200 (grades 7-8)

- **Assessment**
  Your source for blackline master Cloze Activities and Dictation Sentences for the high-use writing words.
  Sourcebook Reviews Words 1–400 (grades 1–4) accompanies *Sourcebook 2*
  Sourcebook Reviews Words 401–800 (grades 5–6) accompanies *Sourcebook 3*
  Sourcebook Reviews Words 801–1200 (grades 7–8) accompanies *Sourcebook 4*

- **Word-Wise Sourcebooks**
  Your source for laugh-aloud rhymes for learning language skills.
  Level 1 *Wordy Birdy* (grades 1–2)
  Level 2 *Willy Wordster* (grades 3–4)
  Level 3 *Inspector Clue-So* (grades 5–6)

VIDEOS

- **Staff Development Video Series**
  Tape I Introduction to Teachers *(85 min.)*
  Tape II Grading and Management (92 min.)
  Tape III Introduction to Parents (37 min.)
  Video Training Guide

- **Free Preview Video**
  On-loan overview
  Call Egger Publishing, Inc.
  toll free: 888-937-7355 *(888-WE-SPELL)*

SEMINAR HANDBOOK

- **Increasing Student Spelling Achievement**

CLASSROOM AIDS

- **My Spell Check K–2**
  Your students' source for an alphabetical listing of 85 high-use writing words with colorful references for animals, numbers, family, clothes, school, days, months, food, and weather. Each package includes a teacher resource of over 50 word activities to extend the word bank, and ten 8 1/2" x 11" coated student cards.

- **Spell Check 3–8**
  Your students' source for an alphabetical listing of 150 high-use writing words with references for months, days, common abbreviations, and 75 context sentences for often-confused words. Each package includes a teacher resource of over 50 word activities to extend the word bank, and ten 8 1/2" x 11" coated student cards.

- **Wall Charts**
  Your source for 5 colorful classroom charts:
  - Alphabetical list of the 100 high-use writing words
  - Context sentences for the "there" homophones
  - Context sentences for the "to" homophones
  - Prefix poem
  - Independent word-study procedure.
  Each package contains all five 18" x 24" wall charts.

TO ORDER
Northwest Textbook
800-676-6630

QUESTIONS

- Call toll free: 888-937-7355 *(888-WE-SPELL)*
- Write to us: Egger Publishing, Inc.
  P.O. Box 12248
  Scottsdale, AZ 85267
- Find us: www.sittonspelling.com
- e-mail Rebecca: rsitton@sittonspelling.com

Dear Educator,

I have created the *Spelling Sourcebook* Series to fulfill four purposes, or needs, for you . . .

First, to show you how to develop your own spelling program. The *Spelling Sourcebook* Series provides the foundation for teacher-customized spelling instruction of the high-frequency writing words to complement any writing-rich classroom. You can develop your own research-based, language-integrated program using the *Spelling Sourcebook* options and resources. Your program will teach students all the basic spelling skills and strategies to spell where it counts . . . in their writing, not just on a test.

Second, to offer you an inservice tool to train teachers to use your new program. *Spelling Sourcebook 1* provides the step-by-step rationale for effectively teaching the program. It is the "staff development" for the program you develop. To complement *Sourcebook 1,* there are two fast-paced training videos with a Training Guide for the facilitator to ensure activity-oriented staff-development sessions that help teachers understand exactly what to do and why. For parents, the 30-minute video "Introduction To Parents" builds community support.

Third, to furnish you with abundant, ready-to-teach ideas. The *Spelling Sourcebook* Series provides a storehouse of language-integrated, skill-based activity options for teaching every one of the 1200 high-frequency writing words listed in its word bank. The activity suggestions reinforce and extend your program to meet your teaching style and the specific needs of your learners.

Fourth, to allow you a cost-effective answer for effective spelling instruction. The *Spelling Sourcebook* Series provides you with a *program,* but not a *workbook spelling program.* A program with student books may needlessly consume the educational budget with few results to show for the time and money spent. The *Spelling Sourcebook* methodology relies on teacher materials, not student books.

To accomplish these purposes, I have developed several *Spelling Sourcebook* teaching materials. There are no student practice books. You don't need them because your students will practice spelling in an authentic format . . . their everyday writing. The focus of *Spelling Sourcebook 1* is how to create and teach a spelling curriculum founded on the highest-frequency writing words. *Spelling Sourcebooks 2, 3,* and *4* are your sources for activity ideas for providing experiences with these high-use words and for teaching all the traditional skills and concepts related to spelling and language facility. This book, the *Spelling Sourcebook Reviews for the High-Use Writing Words 1–400,* provides structured cloze and dictation exercises for a systematic review of previously introduced words to form the foundation for their subsequent transfer and mastery into your students' everyday writing. These materials provide an important component to the program's assessment.

If you have questions, contact me. If you'd like to share your experiences using the *Spelling Sourcebook* Series, contact me. Or if you'd like information on the spelling seminar my associates and I present to educators that highlights the concepts of the *Spelling Sourcebook* methodology, contact me. I'd like to hear from you.

Sincerely,

Rebecca Sitton
P.O. Box 12248
Scottsdale, AZ 85267
(888) WE-SPELL
E-mail: rsitton@sittonspelling.com

Your Guide to the Contents

Using the *Spelling Sourcebook Reviews* 5

Alphabetical List of the High-Use Writing Words 1–400 12

Teaching Notes for the *Spelling Sourcebook Reviews*

Review 1	Core Words 1–5	14	Review 41	Core Words 201–205	47
Review 2	Core Words 6–10	14	Review 42	Core Words 206–210	48
Review 3	Core Words 11–15	15	Review 43	Core Words 211–215	49
Review 4	Core Words 16–20	16	Review 44	Core Words 216–220	50
Review 5	Core Words 21–25	17	Review 45	Core Words 221–225	51
Review 6	Core Words 26–30	17	Review 46	Core Words 226–230	52
Review 7	Core Words 31–35	18	Review 47	Core Words 231–235	53
Review 8	Core Words 36–40	19	Review 48	Core Words 236–240	54
Review 9	Core Words 41–45	20	Review 49	Core Words 241–245	55
Review 10	Core Words 46–50	21	Review 50	Core Words 246–250	56
Review 11	Core Words 51–55	21	Review 51	Core Words 251–255	57
Review 12	Core Words 56–60	22	Review 52	Core Words 256–260	58
Review 13	Core Words 61–65	23	Review 53	Core Words 261–265	58
Review 14	Core Words 66–70	24	Review 54	Core Words 266–270	59
Review 15	Core Words 71–75	25	Review 55	Core Words 271–275	60
Review 16	Core Words 76–80	26	Review 56	Core Words 276–280	61
Review 17	Core Words 81–85	27	Review 57	Core Words 281–285	62
Review 18	Core Words 86–90	27	Review 58	Core Words 286–290	63
Review 19	Core Words 91–95	28	Review 59	Core Words 291–295	64
Review 20	Core Words 96–100	29	Review 60	Core Words 296–300	65
Review 21	Core Words 101–105	30	Review 61	Core Words 301–305	66
Review 22	Core Words 106–110	31	Review 62	Core Words 306–310	67
Review 23	Core Words 111–115	32	Review 63	Core Words 311–315	68
Review 24	Core Words 116–120	32	Review 64	Core Words 316–320	69
Review 25	Core Words 121–125	33	Review 65	Core Words 321–325	70
Review 26	Core Words 126–130	34	Review 66	Core Words 326–330	71
Review 27	Core Words 131–135	35	Review 67	Core Words 331–335	72
Review 28	Core Words 136–140	36	Review 68	Core Words 336–340	73
Review 29	Core Words 141–145	37	Review 69	Core Words 341–345	74
Review 30	Core Words 146–150	38	Review 70	Core Words 346–350	75
Review 31	Core Words 151–155	39	Review 71	Core Words 351–355	76
Review 32	Core Words 156–160	39	Review 72	Core Words 356–360	77
Review 33	Core Words 161–165	40	Review 73	Core Words 361–365	78
Review 34	Core Words 166–170	41	Review 74	Core Words 366–370	79
Review 35	Core Words 171–175	42	Review 75	Core Words 371–375	80
Review 36	Core Words 176–180	43	Review 76	Core Words 376–380	81
Review 37	Core Words 181–185	44	Review 77	Core Words 381–385	82
Review 38	Core Words 186–190	45	Review 78	Core Words 386–390	83
Review 39	Core Words 191–195	46	Review 79	Core Words 391–395	84
Review 40	Core Words 196–200	46	Review 80	Core Words 396–400	85

Blackline Masters
Order Forms

Using the *Spelling Sourcebook Reviews* for the High-Use Writing Words 1–400

What is the purpose of the **Spelling Sourcebook Reviews***?*

The *Reviews* serve two main purposes. They provide in-context spelling practice for students and a spelling assessment opportunity for teachers.

Practice is offered through ongoing review of the high-frequency writing words, the Core Words, and the skills and concepts associated with spelling and language facility. Students need repeated exposure to the high-use words for their ultimate mastery in writing. Using the *Sourcebook* methodology, much of this exposure is afforded through students' everyday writing across the curriculum. The *Reviews* support this natural review through structured, systematic reinforcement activities.

A student's performance on the *Reviews* can be an indicator of spelling development. So the *Reviews* not only provide spelling practice for the high-use writing words, but an opportunity for teachers to evaluate students' progress toward mastering these words in their writing.

How are the **Reviews** *in this book organized to reinforce the high-use writing words 1–400?*

There are 80 lessons in this book of *Spelling Sourcebook Reviews*. Each lesson is organized into two parts: a Cloze Story Review and a Dictation Review. Each Cloze Story Review provides reinforcement for selected high-use writing words within the context of a motivational story. Every one of the 80 cloze stories is correlated to a blackline master for student use (see Blackline Master section in the Appendix of this book). The Dictation Review reinforces words in a controlled-vocabulary sentence story. Each *Review* lesson is supported with complete teaching suggestions in the Teaching Notes.

Each *Review* reinforces five consecutive Core Words on the word frequency list. This book begins with *Review 1* that reinforces words with frequencies 1–5. It continues through *Review 80* that focuses on words 396–400. With the exception of the first *Review*, each lesson also reinforces selected words occurring earlier on the word frequency list. Previous words are chosen systematically to provide maximum exposure for the most frequently misspelled or misused words by student and adult writers. Further, the controlled-vocabulary Dictation Reviews purposely include a few Extra Words that have not yet been introduced as Core Words in the program. These words may be written on the chalkboard and copied by the students for proofreading practice, or they may be included in the dictation for challenge.

How do the **Reviews** *reinforce spelling and language skills and their application in writing?*

Not only do the *Reviews* provide word-specific practice in the cloze and dictation activities, but teaching ideas in the Teaching Notes offer opportunities for the application of spelling in original writing and the reinforcement of spelling and related language skills. Each Cloze Story Review is complemented by a related thinking and writing activity, and all the Dictation Reviews feature a follow-up thinking and writing idea. A section labeled *Extend Learning* follows each Cloze Story Review with teaching suggestions that reinforce skills, such as phonic word patterns, plurals, spelling rules, and understanding homophones.

When should a **Review** *be used?*

The *Reviews* can be used anytime following the introduction of the Core Words they feature. The introduction of the Core Words takes place in a Core Word preview (see *Spelling Sourcebook 1*, Article 4, page 21). The Core Words featured in each *Review* are identified in the Table of Contents of this book, in the Teaching Notes for each *Review*, and on each blackline master. So a *Review* can be used as a teaching tool during a Core Word unit; a *Review* can be used to end a Core Word unit as the counterpart to the Core Word preview; or a *Review* can be used much later to reinforce Core Words from past units that continue to challenge students.

Is it important to use all of each **Review** *with every student?*

All *Reviews* complement students' practice of the words in their everyday writing and teachers' assessment of the words toward mastery. *Reviews* may be used in their entirety, or activities may be selected from a *Review* to provide for specific needs. All students can participate, or certain students can be identified for *Review* activities.

How should a Cloze Story Review be administered?

To use a Cloze Story Review, teachers should first refer to the Teaching Notes for the chosen *Review*. The section labeled *Materials* within each Cloze Story Review identifies the correlated blackline master and the student materials necessary for the activity. Once the Teaching Notes have been perused and the students supplied with their materials, the lesson can begin.

To begin, the cloze story is read from the Teaching Notes by the teacher or by a designated reader as students follow the reading on their copy of the blackline master. The students' pencils are down during this reading. Once read, the story is reread slowly in segments while students write the appropriate words on the numbered cloze story blanks. Then the cloze story is read aloud a final time for students to check their work. Next, students reread the story silently for final proofreading.

Will variations in the administration of the Cloze Story Reviews compromise their effectiveness?

Variations of this process can be used. However for best results, the process used should not vary. It should be concisely explained to students with high expectations for them to follow the process attentively. Requests for repetitions should be denied so that students learn to listen carefully and write expeditiously.

When should the related cloze story activities be completed?

The related cloze story writing activity can be done immediately following the completion of the blackline master, or it can be done later. The section in the Teaching Notes following the cloze story, labeled *Extend Learning,* offers ideas that can be selected for instruction, assigned to all or some students, and discussed during the days that follow.

Is there an alternative format for using the Cloze Story Reviews with students who have spelling challenges?

For students who may become frustrated in their attempt to complete the blackline master cloze activities, modifications can be made. Teachers can simplify an activity by filling in some words or some letters of words in the story blanks for these students. Teachers may use a copy of the original blackline master to fill in the desired assistance. Then this copy can be used to reproduce a modified version of the cloze story that is more appropriate for these students. With this help, all students can participate in the cloze story activities.

How should the Cloze Story Reviews be corrected?

Teachers are empowered to decide how to correct the cloze stories. Students can self-correct their own work or teachers can correct the papers. These suggestions may help.

If the activity is corrected by the students, the correction process becomes another opportunity for learning. Proofreading is reinforced. If this option is used, the correction can follow the general guidelines for correcting the Core Word preview (see *Spelling Sourcebook 1*, Article 4, page 21). Rather than students writing the words in the "rewrite column" for the preview procedure, they fix any misspelled word in the cloze story blank from a model written on the chalkboard.

For another student-correction format, teachers may provide students with a copy of a blackline master with the answers written on the blanks. Then students correct their own cloze story against the story with the answers. Or a transparency could be made from the blackline master that has the answers and projected on a screen using an overhead projector. Then students correct their own paper against the one on the screen. Or a blackline master *without the answers* can be projected onto the screen for students to take turns writing in the correct responses. Then students correct their own papers as the activity is completed on the screen.

Some teachers may prefer to correct the Cloze Story Reviews. This can be done with every cloze story, or announced periodically at the completion of the activity. The student papers can be collected, corrected, and returned; or the papers can be corrected with the individual students, perhaps while the class is completing the related cloze story writing activity. Teachers should also consider the possibility of parent support for the correction of the Cloze Story Reviews.

Can the Cloze Story Reviews contribute toward a student's spelling grade?

The accuracy with which students complete or self-correct their cloze stories can become a portion of their overall spelling grade. Performance on these exercises can be recorded for each grading period. However, the largest part of the total spelling grade must reflect how a student spells in everyday writing. *The only authentic spelling assessment is within writing.*

How should a Dictation Review be administered?

To use a Dictation Review, teachers should first refer to the Teaching Notes for the chosen *Review*. The section labeled *Materials* within each Dictation Review identifies the student materials necessary for the activity. Once the Teaching Notes have been perused and the students supplied with their materials, the lesson can begin.

There are various ways of administering dictation using a traditional dictation format. This method is offered as one successful way. First, all of the sentences are read from the Teaching Notes by the teacher or by a designated reader as students listen. These sentences together form a complete idea. Then the first sentence is read slowly and repeated aloud in unison by the students. The sentence is reread as students listen. Next, students write the sentence from memory. Then the sentence is read again for students to check their work. This procedure is repeated for each of the sentences. At the end of the activity, all the sentences are read a final time for students to check their work. Next, students reread each sentence silently for final proofreading.

Nontraditional formats can also be considered. For example, the sentences can be shared with the students a few days prior to the dictation. Students study and practice the sentences. Then the sentences are dictated in the traditional way. This makes the dictation a criterion-referenced exercise rather than a performance-based activity. In another nontraditional format, the students are provided with the dictation sentences following the dictation, and they are expected to correct all errors themselves. To afford maximum effort from students engaged in this format, students should not be told prior to the dictation, whether their sentences will be teacher-corrected or self-corrected.

Using a variety of dictation formats is suggested, as different formats provide a different kind of practice and assessment information. However, prior to each dictation activity, the student expectations should be concisely stated with high standards for students to follow the process attentively. Requests for repetitions should be denied so that students learn to listen carefully and write expeditiously.

Teachers may allow students to use their Priority Word reference list for some or all of the Dictation Reviews. Or they may disallow use of the reference.

How should the Extra Words be handled?

The words labeled *Extra Words* in the Dictation Review Teaching Notes are words that have not been introduced as Core Words. They can be approached in two ways. The words can be written on the chalkboard prior to the dictation activity and used by the students as a reference as they write their sentences. Repeated opportunities to use a spelling reference reinforces proofreading skills. However, teachers may wish to use the Extra Words for assessment and diagnosis. To explain, teachers can assess how students use the sounds in the words as spelling clues and note if they choose appropriate letters to write those sounds. This, then, provides an informal diagnostic tool for assessing how students attempt to spell new words. This is particularly helpful in the primary grades when phonemic awareness and phonics is a curriculum priority.

When should the Dictation Review follow-up writing activity be completed?

The related dictation follow-up writing activity can be done immediately following the completion of the sentence dictation, or it can be done later. This activity is included in the Teaching Notes following the sentences for dictation and is labeled *Follow-Up Activity*.

Is there an alternative format for using the Dictation Reviews with students who have spelling challenges?

Sentence dictation is often intimidating to students. The dictation should be implemented so that skills are developed comfortably over time. For example, at first teachers can provide the sentences prior to and/or following the dictation. Students can work in pairs to correct their own errors before the sentences are handed in. It makes the dictation easier if teachers tell students how many words are in each sentence. The students count their words prior to the final reading of each sentence and touch each word with the point of their pencil as the sentence is read.

For students who may become overly frustrated in their attempt to complete the dictation activities, more modifications can be made. A teacher-made blackline master can be created with blanks for each word in the sentence. Some words or some letters of words can be filled in. When the sentence dictation activity is administered, these students use a copy of this teacher-made blackline master to write their sentences, rather than using writing paper. As students show dictation progress, less assistance can be provided on the blackline master.

How should the Dictation Reviews be corrected?

Teachers are empowered to decide how to correct the dictation sentences. Students can self-correct their own work or teachers can correct the dictation. These suggestions may help.

If the activity is corrected by the students, the correction process becomes another opportunity for learning. Proofreading is reinforced. If this option is used, students must have access to a correct form of the sentences, such as via a copy of a teacher-made blackline master, on a screen using an overhead projector, a chart, or on the chalkboard. The sentences can simply be provided for self-correction, or a correction activity can be exercised. Students could be selected to write one of their sentences on the chalkboard. Then after any necessary corrections are made, the class uses the sentence on the chalkboard as a model to correct their own sentence.

Some teachers may prefer to correct the Dictation Reviews. This can be done with every dictation, or announced periodically at the completion of the activity. The student papers can be collected, corrected, and returned; or the papers can be corrected with the individual students, perhaps while the class is completing the dictation follow-up writing activity. Teachers should also consider the possibility of parent support for the correction of the Dictation Reviews.

Can the Dictation Reviews contribute toward a student's spelling grade?

The accuracy with which students complete or self-correct their dictation sentences can become a portion of their overall spelling grade. Performance on this exercise can be recorded for each grading period. However, the largest part of the total spelling grade must reflect how a student spells in everyday writing. *The only authentic spelling assessment is within writing.*

*Can the writing activities within the **Reviews** be graded?*

The related writing activities for the Cloze Story Reviews and the Dictation Review follow-up writing activities can be used as one source for a writing sample for a student's Priority Word writing assessment (see *Spelling Sourcebook 1*, Article 9, page 39). The accuracy with which students spell their Priority Words in writing should figure prominently in their final spelling evaluation.

*What follow-up is recommended for mispelled or misused words on a **Review**?*

Once a Cloze Story Review and/or a Dictation Review has been completed and corrected, students may be asked to restudy any misspelled words using the Independent Word-Study Procedure (see *Spelling Sourcebook 1*, Article 6, page 27). If many students were challenged by the same word, it could be placed on an upcoming Core Word preview (see *Spelling Sourcebook 1*, Article 4, page 21). For misused words, such as homophone errors, a discussion of the use of the words is recommended. Appropriate activities selected from *Spelling Sourcebook 2* for words either misspelled or misused could provide additional reinforcement. Further, for teachers complementing their program with the Individualized List of Words (see *Spelling Sourcebook 1*, Article 11, page 49), any misspelled or misused words could be added to this list for further study.

If teachers have questions about using the **Reviews***, what can they do?*

One source for information and ideas about using the *Reviews* is from colleagues who also use the *Spelling Sourcebook* methodology. Teachers networking to help one another solve their own unique problems is a very effective way to become effective users of the program, and specifically the *Reviews*. But if a persistent question creates an obstacle because an answer cannot be found regarding the *Reviews* or any other aspect of the *Spelling Sourcebook* program, the author offers her help. Her home phone number is in the opening letter of all the *Sourcebook* materials. Call her. She is committed to helping dedicated teachers ensure spelling literacy for their students. Every child a speller!

word	frequency	word	frequency	word	frequency	word	frequency
a	4	book	307	every	151	high	224
able	346	both	180	example	261	him	67
about	48	box	388	face	291	himself	277
above	213	boy	205	family	287	his	18
across	247	brought	327	far	222	hold	370
add	335	built	360	fast	376	home	157
after	94	but	31	father	229	horse	385
again	141	by	27	feel	355	hot	368
against	268	called	96	feet	201	house	189
ago	322	came	122	felt	377	how	49
air	160	can	38	few	181	however	250
all	33	can't	380	find	87	hundred	374
almost	216	cannot	343	fine	400	I	24
along	171	car	282	fire	356	I'll	325
also	119	certain	353	first	74	I'm	284
always	183	change	264	fish	299	idea	331
am	397	children	200	five	276	if	44
American	319	city	273	food	198	important	195
among	345	class	391	for	12	in	6
an	39	close	328	form	197	inside	321
and	3	cold	312	found	152	into	61
animal	207	come	123	four	211	is	7
another	121	common	395	from	23	it	10
answer	265	complete	365	front	318	it's	253
any	113	could	70	full	363	its	76
anything	369	country	228	gave	308	just	97
are	15	course	317	get	101	keep	199
area	384	cut	293	give	159	kept	378
around	120	day	114	go	105	kind	214
as	16	did	83	going	192	knew	252
asked	188	didn't	281	good	106	know	100
at	20	different	139	got	219	land	202
away	140	do	45	great	146	large	185
back	103	does	128	green	358	last	166
be	21	dog	347	ground	311	later	288
became	334	don't	190	group	295	learn	271
because	127	done	294	grow	337	learned	326
become	336	door	292	had	29	left	169
been	75	down	84	half	297	less	340
before	332	draw	338	hand	223	let	230
began	215	during	248	hard	242	letter	344
behind	342	each	47	has	62	life	208
being	233	early	324	have	25	light	227
below	176	earth	220	he	11	like	66
best	246	eat	303	head	212	line	161
better	245	end	170	hear	260	list	372
between	154	English	350	heard	262	little	92
big	158	enough	209	help	137	live	217
black	302	even	130	her	64	lived	333
body	285	ever	240	here	134	living	301

word	frequency	word	frequency	word	frequency	word	frequency
long	91	own	163	something	178	town	364
look	117	page	218	soon	236	tree	316
made	81	paper	241	sound	175	true	296
make	72	part	129	space	320	try	254
man	111	people	79	special	361	turn	289
many	55	perhaps	352	stand	387	turned	270
matter	386	person	367	start	389	two	65
may	89	picture	232	state	371	under	164
me	110	piece	392	still	153	United States	305
mean	349	place	131	stood	373	until	196
men	148	plants	300	stop	396	up	50
might	173	play	274	story	237	upon	286
money	279	point	272	strong	381	us	168
more	63	probably	383	study	234	use	88
morning	283	put	138	such	133	usually	278
most	99	ran	362	sun	257	very	93
mother	226	read	165	sure	251	voice	382
move	290	ready	357	surface	393	want	193
much	104	really	313	table	314	was	13
must	126	red	298	take	135	water	90
my	80	remember	315	talk	398	way	86
name	155	rest	351	tell	147	we	36
near	243	right	116	ten	375	well	132
need	221	river	394	than	73	went	143
never	167	room	266	that	9	were	34
new	107	run	306	that's	390	what	32
next	174	sad	323	the	1	when	35
night	231	said	43	their	42	where	98
no	71	same	115	them	52	whether	399
not	30	saw	177	then	53	which	41
nothing	329	say	149	there	37	while	172
notice	379	school	194	these	58	white	239
now	78	sea	267	they	19	who	77
number	145	second	235	thing	258	whole	259
of	2	see	68	think	118	why	136
off	142	seen	280	this	22	will	46
often	186	sentence	244	those	182	wind	341
oh	366	set	162	though	330	with	17
old	144	several	263	thought	179	without	204
on	14	she	54	three	125	words	95
once	206	short	304	through	102	work	124
one	28	should	156	time	69	world	191
only	85	show	184	to	5	would	59
open	310	shown	348	today	249	write	108
or	26	side	203	together	187	year	225
order	309	since	238	told	255	yes	359
other	60	six	354	too	112	yet	339
our	109	small	150	took	210	you	8
out	51	so	57	top	269	young	256
over	82	some	56	toward	275	your	40

REVIEW 1

CLOZE STORY REVIEW 1

Materials: Master 1, pencil, story paper, crayons

Core Words

the	1	and	3	to	5
of	2	a	4		

Tell students that this is a story about two hippopotamus animal friends. Discuss hippos. Then read the story as students write the words. Discuss possible answers to the story question. Then have students write their answer on story paper and draw the hippo friends.

Friends

Friends are nice (1) <u>to</u> each other. They help each other. George (2) <u>and</u> Martha are two hippo friends. George was hungry. Martha fixed George (3) <u>a</u> bowl (4) <u>of</u> soup. But George didn't like (5) <u>the</u> soup. If you were George, what would you do?

■ Extend Learning

1. Have students share their answer to the story question and their picture. Then read *George and Martha* by James Marshall that tells how George solved this problem. Marshall has several books about these two hippo friends.
2. Discuss *to* and *two.* Have students circle *two* and *to* in the story. Post context sentences on the wall for these difficult homophones. (You may wish to wait to present *too*).
3. Have students find and circle the story words *you, was, are, they.* These words will soon be introduced as Core Words.
4. Have students circle the capitals at the beginning of each sentence in the story. Ask them to identify other words in the story that have capitals (George, Martha). Discuss capitals at the beginning of each sentence and capitals for the beginning letter of a name. Discuss the punctuation at the end of each sentence. Discuss the question mark. Have students find another question sentence in a story book. Then have them read their question sentence to a partner.

DICTATION REVIEW 1

Materials: pencil, writing paper

Core Words

the	1	and	3	to	5
of	2	a	4		

Extra Words

give, me, cup, milk, you, I, like, drink
(See page 9 for ideas for handling Extra Words.)

Remind students to capitalize the first letter in each sentence. Have students write the sentences as they are dictated.

1. Give me a cup of the milk.
2. You and I like to drink milk.

■ Follow-Up Activity

Ask students to write a sentence that tells about something they like to drink when they are thirsty.

REVIEW 2

CLOZE STORY REVIEW 2

Materials: Master 2, pencil, story paper, crayons

Core Words

in	6	you	8	it	10
is	7	that	9		

Review Core Words

of (2), and (3)

Tell students that this is a guessing-game story. Review capital letters at the beginning of each sentence. Read the story as students write the words. Discuss possible answers to the story question. Then ask students to write their answer in a sentence on story paper and draw the pet this story describes.

A Good Pet

This (1) <u>is</u> an animal (2) <u>that</u> makes a good pet. (3) <u>You</u> might give this animal a dish (4) <u>of</u> milk. This animal looks for mice. This animal may climb the fence (5) <u>and</u> walk along (6) <u>it</u>. This animal may live (7) <u>in</u> your house or live outside. This animal purrs. What could this be?

■ Extend Learning

1. Have students share their answer to the story question and their picture. Have them discuss the story clues that led them to their answer.
2. Have students circle and write the review story words *a* and *the*.
3. Have students find and circle the high-use story word *this* each of the seven times it occurs in the story.
4. Ask students to circle and write the story word *outside*. Discuss its antonym *inside*. Write *inside* and *outside* on the chalkboard. Ask students to name inside and outside pets. Write the animals in the appropriate column asking students to predict the letters as the words are written.
5. Have students circle and write the story word that rhymes with *cat* (that). Review the *Spelling Sourcebook 2* rhyming activity with *that*. Extend it by asking students to circle and write the two occurrences of the story word *may*. Then write more ___ay words.

DICTATION REVIEW 2

Materials: pencil, writing paper

Core Words

in	6	you	8	it	10
is	7	that	9		

Review Core Words

the (1), to (5)

Extra Words

book, bag, can, read, me (See page 9 for ideas for handling Extra Words.)

Remind students to capitalize the first letter in each sentence. Have students write the sentences as they are dictated.

1. The book is in that bag.
2. You can read it to me.

■ Follow-Up Activity

Show students a closed bag containing a familiar book that could be read by most students. Provide clues for the book's title. Ask students to write a sentence telling which book they think it might be. Then reveal the book.

REVIEW 3 — Core Words 11–15

Use after Core Word 15

CLOZE STORY REVIEW 3

Materials: Master 3, pencil, story paper, crayons

Core Words

he	11	was	13	are	15
for	12	on	14		

Review Core Words

of (2), that (9)

Tell students that this is a story about a man who sells caps, or hats. Review capital letters at the beginning of each sentence. Read the story as students write the words. Discuss possible answers to the story question. Then ask students to write their answer to the story question and draw the man wearing all his caps.

Caps

There (1) <u>was</u> a man who had many caps (2) <u>for</u> sale. All these caps were (3) <u>on</u> his head. But no one wanted to buy any (4) <u>of</u> his caps. "These (5) <u>are</u> fine caps! I must sell them," said the man. (6) <u>He</u> needs help. Do you have an idea or two (7) <u>that</u> could help him?

■ Extend Learning

1. Have students share their answer to the story question and their picture. Then read *Caps for Sale* by Esphyr Slobodkina. This story is the tale of this cap peddler and some monkeys and their monkey business.
2. Discuss the word *cap* and its synonyms, such as *hat, bonnet, beret*. Discuss different kinds of caps, such as *baseball cap, stocking cap, painter's cap*.
3. Have students circle and write the story words that begin with *th* (there, these, them, the, that).
4. Have students circle and write the review story words *a, to, you, that*. Have students circle and write the story word *two*. Review *to* and *two*.
5. Have students find and circle the punctuation at the end of each story sentence. Discuss the use of the period, exclamation mark, and question mark. Write sentences on the chalkboard to illustrate the use of each of these marks.

DICTATION REVIEW 3

Materials: pencil, writing paper

Core Words

he	11	was	13	are	15
for	12	on	14		

Review Core Words

the (1), you (8)

Extra Words

Dan, reads, fun, reading, bus, like (See page 9 for ideas for handling Extra Words.)

Review use of the question mark. Remind students to capitalize the first letter in each sentence and the first letter in a name. Have students write the sentences as they are dictated.

1. Dan reads for fun.
2. He was reading on the bus.
3. Are you like Dan?

■ Follow-Up Activity

Ask students to write a sentence that tells about their favorite place to read a good book.

REVIEW 4   Core Words 16–20

Use after Core Word 20

CLOZE STORY REVIEW 4

Materials: Master 4, pencil, story paper, crayons

Core Words

as	16	his	18	at	20
with	17	they	19		

Review Core Words

to (5), on (14)

Tell students that this is a story about a lion named Dandelion. Discuss the story title and the meaning of *dandy.* Review capital letters at the beginning of each sentence. Read the story as students write the words. Discuss possible answers to the story question. Then have students write their answer to the story question and draw Dandelion in his fancy party clothes.

A Dandy Dandelion

Jennifer Giraffe invited Dandelion the Lion (1) <u>to</u> a party. He fixed (2) <u>his</u> hair and put (3) <u>on</u> new clothes. Dandelion looked (4) <u>as</u> if he could be in movies! Dandelion took flowers (5) <u>with</u> him. (6) <u>They</u> were for Jennifer. But when he was (7) <u>at</u> her door, she didn't know him. Why?

■ Extend Learning

1. Have students share their answer to the story question and their picture. Then read *Dandelion* by Don Freeman to see how the rain turned Dandelion back into the lion that Jennifer and his friends recognized and loved.
2. Discuss the yellow weed flowers, dandelions. Then have students write why a lion might be called the name Dandelion. Share the responses.
3. Have students circle and write the review story words *a, and, in, he, for, was.*
4. Identify selected story homophones with the students. Choices may include *to, for, be, hair, clothes, know, new.* Write the homophone partner words on the chalkboard as students predict their spellings. Then review the word meanings. You may wish to wait to introduce *too.*

DICTATION REVIEW 4

Materials: pencil, writing paper

Core Words

as	16	his	18	at	20
with	17	they	19		

Review Core Words

the (1), was (13)

Extra Words

Tom, dog, were, park, can, run, fast

Review use of the question mark. Remind students to capitalize the first letter in each sentence and the first letter in a name. Have students write the sentences as they are dictated.

1. Tom was with his dog.
2. They were at the park.
3. Can Tom run as fast as his dog?

■ **Follow-Up Activity**

Discuss possible answers to the question posed. Then ask students to tell in writing what they think Tom and his dog might have been doing for fun together at the park.

REVIEW 5 — Core Words 21–25

Use after Core Word 25

CLOZE STORY REVIEW 5

Materials: Master 5, pencil, story paper, crayons

Core Words

be	21	from	23	have	25
this	22	I	24		

Review Core Words

of (2), are (15)

Tell students that this story is a math puzzle. Review capital letters at the beginning of each sentence. Read the story puzzle as students write the words. Discuss strategies for solving the puzzle and let students suggest what these colored objects may be. Have students solve the puzzle independently or as a class activity. Then have students write the answer to the story question and draw and color the story objects.

A Number Game

Mine is red. The two (1) <u>of</u> yours look blue. The boys (2) <u>have</u> four green ones. (3) <u>This</u> orange and yellow one is Kay's. She got it (4) <u>from</u> Mike. How many (5) <u>are</u> there in all? (6) <u>I</u> would like to know. (7) <u>Be</u> sure that you count carefully.

■ **Extend Learning**

1. Have students share their answer to the story question and their picture. Review the method for arriving at the correct answer, eight.
2. Have students circle and write the story words *to* and *two*. Contrast their use. Write the number words one–ten on the chalkboard as students predict their spellings. Identify the homophones among the number words (one, two, four, eight). Discuss the spellings and meanings of the homophones of these number words. You may wish to wait to introduce *too*.

3. Have students circle and write the color words in the story (red, blue, orange, green, yellow.) Then have students name more color words. Write the words on the chalkboard as students predict their spellings.
4. Have students circle and write the review story words *the, to, is, you, that, it, and, in.*
5. Have students write another number-game story to challenge their classmates.

DICTATION REVIEW 5

Materials: pencil, writing paper

Core Words

be	21	from	23	have	25
this	22	I	24		

Review Core Words

a (4), to (5), in (6), is (7), you (8), it (10)

Extra Words

box, me, what, could

Review use of the question mark. Remind students to capitalize the first letter in each sentence and the first letter in a name. Have students write the sentences as they are dictated.

1. I have a box.
2. This box is from me to you.
3. What could be in it?

■ **Follow-Up Activity**

Hide something inside a box. Let students hold and shake the box. Then ask students to write what they think could be in it.

REVIEW 6 — Core Words 26–30

Use after Core Word 30

CLOZE STORY REVIEW 6

Materials: Master 6, pencil, story paper, crayons

Core Words

or	26	one	28	not	30
by	27	had	29		

Review Core Words

and (3), they (19)

Tell students that this is a guessing-game story. Review capital letters at the beginning of each sentence. Read the story as students write the words. Discuss possible answers to the story question, confirming *elephants* as the correct answer. Write *elephants* on the chalkboard as students predict the spelling. Then have students write their answer to the story question and draw a huge elephant.

The Largest Land Animals

Which land animal is today's biggest? You may have (1) <u>had</u> the chance to see these big animals in a zoo (2) <u>or</u> animal park. You might have seen (3) <u>one</u> go (4) <u>by</u> in a parade. (5) <u>They</u> have large ears (6) <u>and</u> a small tail. These huge animals do (7) <u>not</u> make good house pets.

■ Extend Learning

1. Have students share their answer to the story question and their picture. The largest living land animals are the African elephants. Help students locate information about the two kinds of elephants (African and Asiatic). Students may wish to explore the interesting differences between these two large beasts.
2. Have students circle and write the story words *big, huge,* and *large.* Then brainstorm for synonyms for these words. Choices may include *great, gigantic, enormous, immense, jumbo.* Then have them circle and write a story word opposite (*small*).
3. Identify selected story word homophones with the students. Choices may include *one, you, see, to, might, or, by, tail, not, seen, do.* Write the homophone pairs on the chalkboard as students predict their spellings. Discuss the meanings of the words. You may wish to wait to introduce *too.*
4. Have students circle and write the review story words *is, you, have, the, to, in, a.*

DICTATION REVIEW 6

Materials: pencil, writing paper

Core Words

| or | 26 | one | 28 | not | 30 |
| by | 27 | had | 29 | | |

Review Core Words

the (1), and (3), a (4), his (18), they (19)

Extra Words

Bob, dog, cat, day, could, find, were, door

Remind students to capitalize the first letter in each sentence and the first letter in a name. Have students write the sentences as they are dictated.

1. Bob had a dog and a cat.
2. One day Bob could not find his dog or cat.
3. They were not by the door.

■ Follow-Up Activity

Discuss possible ways Bob might find his dog and cat. Ask students to tell in writing about a real or make-believe experience finding a pet.

REVIEW 7 Core Words 31–35

Use after Core Word 35

CLOZE STORY REVIEW 7

Materials: Master 7, pencil, story paper, crayons

Core Words

| but | 31 | all | 33 | when | 35 |
| what | 32 | were | 34 | | |

Review Core Words

with (17), one (28)

Tell students that this is a story about Peter and his new baby sister. Review capital letters at the beginning of each sentence. Read the story as students write the words. Discuss the joy of having a new brother or sister. Then discuss how some things change when a new baby comes home. Talk about possible answers to the story question. Then have students write their answer to the story question and draw Peter having fun in a quiet way.

Peter's Fun

Peter has a new baby sister. Now (1) <u>when</u> he plays, he has to be quiet. He cannot be noisy. (2) <u>One</u> day he made two tall buildings (3) <u>with</u> his blocks, (4) <u>but</u> they (5) <u>all</u> came crashing down! Mother told Peter that the blocks (6) <u>were</u> noisy. (7) <u>What</u> might Peter do for quiet fun?

Extend Learning

1. Have students share their answer to the story question and their picture. Then read *Peter's Chair* by Ezra Jack Keats to see how Peter solved his "new sister" problem in a positive way.

2. Have students circle the story words *quiet* and *noisy*. Identify these words as antonyms. Then ask students to find other words in the story for which they could name an antonym. Choices may include *day/night, new/old, sister/brother, he/she, his/her, tall/short, down/up, mother/father*. Write the antonyms on the chalkboard as students predict their spellings.

3. Have students circle and write the review story words *a, he, to, be, they, that, the, for*. Then have them circle and write the story word *cannot* and underline the review word *can* inside of *cannot*. Discuss compound words and have students find and write examples of compounds.

4. Have students circle and write the story words *to* and *two*. Then have them write sentences using these homophones.

DICTATION REVIEW 7

Materials: pencil, writing paper

Core Words

but	31	all	33	when	35
what	32	were	34		

Review Core Words

to (5), you (8), was (13), they (19), I (24), not (30)

Extra Words

doing, fell, running, fast, came, help, me

Review use of the question mark. Remind students to capitalize the first letter in each sentence. Have students write the sentences as they are dictated. Provide assistance with the comma in the second sentence.

1. What were you doing when you fell?
2. I was running, but not fast.
3. They all came to help me.

Follow-Up Activity

Ask students to tell in writing about a time when they fell and needed help.

CLOZE STORY REVIEW 8

Materials: Master 8, pencil, story paper, crayons

Core Words

we	36	can	38	your	40
there	37	an	39		

Review Core Words

what (32), when (35)

Tell students this is a story about how the weather often changes. Review capital letters at the beginning of each sentence. Read the story as students write the words. Discuss weather forecasting and the current weather. Then have students write their answer to the story question and draw their favorite kind of weather day.

The Weather

The sun may be shining as (1) <u>we</u> go to school. Then (2) <u>when</u> school is out, (3) <u>there</u> are big rain clouds! You needed (4) <u>an</u> umbrella after all! The weather (5) <u>can</u> fool us. Now it's (6) <u>your</u> turn to predict our weather. (7) <u>What</u> will the weather be like tomorrow at two o'clock?

Extend Learning

1. Have students share their answer to the story question and their picture. Then have students check the weather the next day to assess their weather predictions.

2. Review the familiar rhyme, *The Eensy, Weensy Spider*. In this old rhyme the unpredictable weather plays an important role in the spider's day. Ask students if they can identify other stories or poems in which there were weather surprises.

3. Ask students to circle and write the review story words *the, be, as, to, is, you, all, at*.

4. Have students circle and write the story words *are* and *our*. Discuss their use. Then have students write sentences using these often-confused words.

5. Have students circle and write the story words *to* and *two*. Then have them explain orally to a partner how the words are used to mean something different.

DICTATION REVIEW 8

Materials: pencil, writing paper

Core Words

we	36	can	38	your	40
there	37	an	39		

Review Core Words

to (5), you (8), be (21), I (24), by (27)

Extra Words

will, see, team, play, come, hour, early, want, sit

Review use of the question mark. Remind students to capitalize the first letter in each sentence. Have students write the sentences as they are dictated.

1. We will be there to see your team play.
2. Can we come an hour early?
3. I want to sit by you.

■ Follow-Up Activity

Discuss what this team event might be. List possibilities on the chalkboard in which teams participate. Ask students to predict the spellings of the words as they are written. Then ask students to tell in writing about a team event they attended.

REVIEW 9 Core Words 41–45

Use after Core Word 45

CLOZE STORY REVIEW 9

Materials: Master 9, pencil, story paper, crayons

Core Words

which	41	said	43	do	45
their	42	if	44		

Review Core Words

were (34), there (37)

Tell students that this story is about a famous race between two animals. Review *there* and *their.* Read the story as students write the words. Discuss the tale and its surprise ending. Then have students write their answer to the story question, explain the winning strategy, and draw some part of the race.

The Race

(1) <u>There</u> is an old story about a race between a hare and a tortoise. The hare (2) <u>said</u> that he would win! To begin, the two animals put (3) <u>their</u> toes at the starting line. Then they (4) <u>were</u> off! (5) <u>Which</u> animal (6) <u>do</u> you think won? (7) <u>If</u> you know this tale, you know its surprise ending.

■ Extend Learning

1. Have students share their answer to the story question and their picture. Then direct students to storybooks in which this old tale is told. Have students read the tale. Then have them retell the tale to one another.
2. Point out the synonyms *story* and *tale.* Ask students to identify another word for *hare* (rabbit) and *tortoise* (turtle).
3. Have students circle and write the story words *to* and *two.* Then have them circle and write *there* and *their.* Have students write these homophones in sentences.
4. Have students circle and write the story word *off.* Remove an *f* to make *of.* Contrast *of* and *off.* Have students write sentences using the look-alike words.
5. Have students circle and write the story word antonyms *starting* and *ending.* Then have them identify antonyms for the story words *old, win, won, off.*

DICTATION REVIEW 9

Materials: pencil, writing paper

Core Words

which	41	said	43	do	45
their	42	if	44		

Review Core Words

the (1), to (5), is (7), they (19), not (30), what (32), we (36), there (37)

Extra Words

take, bus, school, know

Review use of the question mark. Remind students to capitalize the first letter in each sentence. Have students write the sentences as they are dictated.

1. They said to take the bus to their school.
2. Do we know which bus we take?
3. What if the bus is not there?

■ **Follow-Up Activity**

Discuss ways of getting to and from school. Talk about the pros and cons of taking a school or city bus to school. Have students write about how they get to and from school.

REVIEW 10 · Core Words 46–50

Use after Core Word 50

CLOZE STORY REVIEW 10

Materials: Master 10, pencil, writing paper, art paper, scissors, crayons

Core Words

will	46	about	48	up	50
each	47	how	49		

Review Core Words

and (3), this (22), have (25), what (32), your (40)

Tell students that this is a story about how to make a bookmark. Review capitals at the beginning of each sentence. Read the story as students write the words. Then have students write their answer to the story question.

Make a Bookmark

I (1) <u>will</u> tell you (2) <u>how</u> to make a beautiful bookmark. (3) <u>Each</u> of you needs paper, scissors, (4) <u>and</u> crayons. Cut the paper to (5) <u>about</u> the size you want the bookmark. Write (6) <u>your</u> name (7) <u>up</u> at the top of the paper. Then decorate (8) <u>this</u> paper by drawing pretty goldfish or seashells. Now you (9) <u>have</u> a fine bookmark! (10) <u>What</u> can you do with your bookmark?

■ **Extend Learning**

1. Have students share their answer to the story question and their picture. Then have students make a bookmark.
2. Have students circle and write the story words with final silent *e*. Students should identify *make, size, write, name, fine, have*. Discuss the *long-vowel-final-silent e* connection. Discuss the exception to the regular pattern, *have*. Then have students find and write more words that follow the regular pattern or are exceptions to it.

3. Write the compound word *bookmark* on the chalkboard and underline the two word parts. Have students find and circle two more compound story words (goldfish, seashells). Then brainstorm for more compounds. Write the words on the chalkboard as students predict the letters.
4. Have students find and circle the question mark and the exclamation mark in the story. Then have them write a sentence using a question mark and another using an exclamation. Have students share their sentences with a partner.

DICTATION REVIEW 10

Materials: pencil, writing paper

Core Words

will	46	about	48	up	50
each	47	how	49		

Review Core Words

of (2), for (12), they (19), what (32), when (35), your (40), their (42), do (45)

Extra Words

friends, get, like, eggs, milk, them

Review use of the question mark. Remind students to capitalize the first letter in each sentence. Have students write the sentences as they are dictated.

1. When will your friends get up?
2. How do they like their eggs?
3. What about milk for each of them?

■ **Follow-Up Activity**

Discuss the importance of breakfast. Then ask students to tell in writing about their favorite breakfast.

REVIEW 11 · Core Words 51–55

Use after Core Word 55

CLOZE STORY REVIEW 11

Materials: Master 11, pencil, story paper, crayons

Core Words

out	51	then	53	many	55
them	52	she	54		

Review Core Words

were (34), when (35), there (37), their (42), said (43)

Tell students this is a story about a little hen that they may know. Review *there* and *their*. Read the story as students write the words. Discuss this familiar tale and its ending. Then have students write their answer to the story question and draw the Little Red Hen.

The Little Red Hen Makes Bread

Once (1) <u>there</u> was a hen called the Little Red Hen. (2) <u>She</u> wanted to make bread. This hen had (3) <u>many</u> friends. The hen asked (4) <u>them</u> for (5) <u>their</u> help. They all (6) <u>said</u> that they (7) <u>were</u> busy. So the hen made two loaves of bread herself. (8) <u>When</u> the hot loaves came (9) <u>out</u> of the oven, they smelled so good! (10) <u>Then</u> what do you think happened next?

■ **Extend Learning**

1. Have students share their answer to the story question and their picture. Direct students to storybooks in which this old tale is told. Have students read the tale. Then have them retell the tale to one another.
2. Have students circle and write the story words *their* and *there*. Then have them circle and write *to* and *two*. Discuss the meanings of these homophones. Have students write these words in sentences.
3. Have students write *then* and *when*. Then have them circle *hen* inside of each. Have students circle and write another story word that has a word inside of it. Share the students' choices on the chalkboard.
4. Have students find and circle the two story words *so*. Discuss the different meanings of this word in the story.

DICTATION REVIEW 11

Materials: pencil, writing paper

Core Words

out	51	then	53	many	55
them	52	she	54		

Review Core Words

to (5), in (6), for (12), was (13), with (17), I (24), have (25), had (29), said (43)

Extra Words

friends, playing, my, mother, come, dinner, me

Have students write the sentences as they are dictated.
1. I have many friends.
2. I was out playing with them.
3. Then my mother said to come in.
4. She had dinner for me.

■ **Follow-Up Activity**

Discuss what students do when they are out playing with their friends. Then have students tell in writing what they like to do most to have fun with their friends outdoors.

REVIEW 12 | Core Words 56–60

Use after Core Word 60

CLOZE STORY REVIEW 12

Materials: Master 12, pencil, story paper, crayons

Core Words

some	56	these	58	other	60
so	57	would	59		

Review Core Words

have (25), when (35), there (37), their (42), then (53)

Tell students that this story tells about bears. Review *there* and *their*. Read the story as students write the words. Discuss food sources for bears, such as grasses, berries, roots, bugs, fish, honey. Write the words on the chalkboard as students predict their spellings. Then have students write their answer to the story question using the words on the chalkboard for reference and draw the bears eating one of their favorite foods.

Bears

(1) <u>There</u> are (2) <u>some</u> animals that sleep all winter. They hibernate. Bears hibernate in (3) <u>their</u> dens. (4) <u>Then</u> in the spring they wake up (5) <u>so</u> that they can play and eat. They like to see each (6) <u>other</u>. (7) <u>When</u> the bears leave the dens, they are hungry. What do you think (8) <u>these</u> bears (9) <u>would</u> like to eat? Do you (10) <u>have</u> an idea?

■ Extend Learning

1. Have students share their answer to the story question and their picture.
2. Have students circle and write the story words *their* and *there*. Review the meanings of these homophones. Have students find a sentence in a book that uses *their* or *there*. Then have students read their sentence to a partner. The partner determines which homophone is used in the sentence.
3. Have students circle and write the review story word *each*. Have students make new words by adding beginning letters, such as *beach, bleach, peach, preach, reach, teach*. Contrast the *ea* sound in the story words *each, eat, leave* with the *ea* in *bear*.
4. Ask students how they would find out about other animals that hibernate in winter, such as squirrels. List these information sources on the chalkboard. Encourage interested students to pursue the information and report what they learn to the class.
5. Have students predict the spellings through the word preview procedure of the review story words *they, each, are, what* and the new story words *bears, spring, play, eat*. Have students check their predictions against the spelling of the story words.

DICTATION REVIEW 12

Materials: pencil, writing paper

Core Words

some	56	these	58	other	60
so	57	would	59		

Review Core Words

to (5), you (8), are (15), be (21), one(s) (28), can (38), which (41), do (45)

Extra Words

books, funny, make, laugh, sad, like, read

Have students write the sentences as they are dictated.
1. Some books are so funny.
2. These books would make you laugh.
3. Other books can be sad.
4. Which ones do you like to read?

■ Follow-Up Activity

Discuss both funny and sad books. Ask students what makes books funny or sad. Have students tell in writing about their favorite funny or sad book.

REVIEW 13 Core Words 61–65

Use after Core Word 65

CLOZE STORY REVIEW 13

Materials: Master 13, pencil, writing paper

Core Words

into	61	more	63	two	65
has	62	her	64		

Review Core Words

to (5), there (37), their (42), said (43), many (55)

Tell students that this is a story about two mice friends who live very different lives. Review *there* and *their; two* and *to*. Read the story as students write the words. Discuss possible answers to the story questions. Then have students write their answer to the story questions and draw the mouse they think has the best life.

> ### Happy Mice
>
> I'd like you (1) <u>to</u> meet (2) <u>two</u> mice. (3) <u>Their</u> lives are quite different. One lives happily in (4) <u>her</u> country cottage. "(5) <u>There</u> is (6) <u>more</u> fresh air in the country," she (7) <u>said</u>. The other mouse lives well in the busy city. "Come (8) <u>into</u> the city. You will like the (9) <u>many</u> things to see and do," the city mouse replied. Which mouse do you think (10) <u>has</u> the best life? Why?

■ Extend Learning

1. Have students share their answer to the story questions and their picture.
2. Have students find and circle the two occurrences of the story word *lives*. Discuss the two pronunciations of the homograph. Discuss other homographs (words that are spelled the same, but have different pronunciations and meanings), such as *read, wind, does, close, use*.
3. Have students circle and write a story word contraction (I'd). Then have them write the two review words in the contraction (I, would). Have students write the review words *he, she, we, they*. Then have them use *would* with each word to write more contractions.

4. Have students circle and write the story words *mouse* and *mice*. Then help students identify other irregular plurals, such as *man/men, woman/women, child/children, foot/feet, tooth/teeth.* Write the words on the chalkboard as students predict their spellings.

5. Have students circle and write the review story word *other.* Then have them write *mother, brother, another.* Next, have them circle and write the review story word *which.* Then have students list other words that begin with *wh,* such as *what, when, why, where.*

DICTATION REVIEW 13

Materials: pencil, writing paper

Core Words

into	61	more	63	two	65
has	62	her	64		

Review Core Words

in (6), it (10), had (29), how (49), then (53), she (54), many (55)

Extra Words

apples, basket, put, four, now

Have students write the sentences as they are dictated.
1. She had two apples in her basket.
2. Then she put four more into it.
3. How many apples has she now?

■ Follow-Up Activity

Discuss the strategy for answering the question. Then have students write their answer to the question. Select students to write another math story in which a computation question is posed. Provide time for sharing the stories.

REVIEW 14   Core Words 66–70

Use after Core Word 70

CLOZE STORY REVIEW 14

Materials: Master 14, pencil, story paper, crayons

Core Words

like	66	see	68	could	70
him	67	time	69		

Review Core Words

that (9), are (15), from (23), your (40), would (59)

Tell students that this is a story about writing letters to friends. Read the story as students write the words. Then have students write their answer to the story question and draw a picture of the person receiving their friendly letter.

Friends and Letters

Do you have a friend (1) <u>that</u> you do not (2) <u>see</u> often? Perhaps you (3) <u>could</u> write to her or (4) <u>him</u>. It (5) <u>would</u> take only a short while to write this letter. It should take only a minute for (6) <u>your</u> friend to read the letter. Letters (7) <u>are</u> a good way to make our friendships last for a long, long (8) <u>time</u>. Who might (9) <u>like</u> to get a friendly letter (10) <u>from</u> you?

■ Extend Learning

1. Have students share their answer to the story question and their picture.

2. Create an easy-to-follow letter format on the chalkboard. Have students follow this format to write a short friendly letter. Remind students to proofread their letter.

3. Have students circle and write the story words *could, would, should.* Ask students to find and write more words with *ou.* Choices may include *you, your, about, out, our, through, around, house, four, country.* Have students underline the *ou* in each word. Then conclude that the *ou* makes many different sounds in words and is an unreliable spelling aid. In fact, the *ou* is the most deviant vowel sound in the English language.

4. Have students circle and write the story words *time, write, while, make, like.* Identify the long vowel sound in each word and the final silent *e.* Point out that many words with the final silent *e* have the long vowel sound. The story word *have* is an exception. Ask students to find and write more words that follow this *long-vowel-final-silent e* pattern.

5. Have students circle and write the often-confused story words *are* and *our.* Contrast their use. Have students write a sentence using each one.

DICTATION REVIEW 14

Materials: pencil, writing paper

Core Words

like	66	see	68	could	70
him	67	time	69		

Review Core Words

the (1), of (2), to (5), be (21), I (24), what (32), there (37), will (46), would (59), other(s) (60), two (65)

Extra Words

very, much, us, go

Have students write the sentences as they are dictated.
1. I would like to see him very much.
2. What time could the two of us go?
3. Will there be others there?

■ Follow-Up Activity

Have students identify someone they would like to see this weekend. Then have them tell in writing who that person is and what they would do together.

REVIEW 15   Core Words 71–75

Use after Core Word 75

CLOZE STORY REVIEW 15

Materials: Master 15, pencil, story paper, crayons

Core Words

no	71	than	73	been	75
make	72	first	74		

Review Core Words

but (31), were (34), there (37), their (42), could (70)

Tell students this is a story about loosing baby teeth. Review *there* and *their, then* and *than.* Read the story as students write the words. Then have students write their answers to the story questions and draw their solution to Arthur's problem.

The Loose Tooth

(1) <u>First</u> one tooth fell out and then another! All the students (2) <u>were</u> losing (3) <u>their</u> baby teeth (4) <u>but</u> Arthur. Arthur had (5) <u>been</u> wiggling his loose tooth for a long time. More (6) <u>than</u> anything, Arthur wished he (7) <u>could</u> get this tooth out. But (8) <u>no</u> amount of wiggling seemed to (9) <u>make</u> it come loose. Is (10) <u>there</u> help for poor Arthur? How might he get his tooth out?

■ Extend Learning

1. Have students share their answers to the story questions. Then read *Arthur's Tooth* by Marc Brown to students. Poor Arthur is uncomfortable because he isn't loosing his teeth like his classmates. Suggestions are offered. Compare these suggestions with those the students write.

2. Have students circle and write the often-confused story words *then* and *than.* Discuss the difference in meaning. Then have students write sentences using the words.

3. Have students circle and write the story words *there* and *their.* Then have them write a sentence using each, but writing a blank in place of these words. Have students exchange sentences and fill in the blanks with the correct homophones.

4. Have students circle and write the story words *tooth* and *teeth.* Review *mouse* and *mice* (Lesson 13) and other irregular plurals.

5. Have students circle and write the review story word *out.* Then write its opposite (in). Next have students work in pairs to list more antonym pairs. Provide time to share the lists.

DICTATION REVIEW 15

Materials: pencil, writing paper

Core Words

no	71	than	73	been	75
make(ing)	72	first	74		

Review Core Words

the (1), of (2), to (5), is (7), for (12), be (21), I (24), have (25), or (26), one (28), there (37), them (52), some (56), would (59), has (62), two (65), like (66)

Extra Words

June, good, cookies, us, way, better

Review *to* and *two*. Review adding the *ing* suffix to a word ending in silent *e* (make/making). Have students write the sentences as they are dictated.

1. June has been making some good cookies for us.
2. There is no way to make them better than June.
3. I would like to be the first to have one or two of them.

■ **Follow-Up Activity**

Discuss the students' favorite kinds of cookies. Then have students create a poster advertisement for their favorite kind of cookie.

REVIEW 16   Core Words 76–80

Use after Core Word 80

CLOZE STORY REVIEW 16

Materials: Master 16, pencil, writing paper

Core Words

its	76	now	78	my	80
who	77	people	79		

Review Core Words

there (37), their (42), then (53), than (73), first (74)

Tell students that this is a story about a special way to paint a picture. Review *there* and *their, then* and *than*. Read the story as students write the words. Then have students tell in writing whether they think they would or would not want to try straw painting.

Straw Painting

Many (1) <u>people</u> (2) <u>who</u> have never painted before are straw painting (3) <u>now</u>. Two of (4) <u>my</u> friends tried it. (5) <u>First</u> they put some paint drops on paper. (6) <u>Then</u> they blew through one end of a straw. Air came out (7) <u>its</u> other end. The air blew the paint drops here and (8) <u>there</u> to make (9) <u>their</u> picture. "Wow! It's more fun (10) <u>than</u> brush painting!" they all said.

■ **Extend Learning**

1. Have students share their answer to the question about straw painting. Then provide materials for students who wish to straw paint. Have them write the directions for creating a straw-painting picture. Provide time for sharing the directions to verify their accuracy.
2. Have students circle and write the story words *there, their, its, it's, to, two, then, than.* Use the words in oral and written sentences to differentiate the word pairs.
3. Discuss the story word *blew* and the color word *blue.* Contrast the homophones.
4. Have students name ways to create a picture without paint. Choices may include crayons, chalk, marking pens, pencils. Write their answers on the chalkboard as students predict the letters of the words.
5. Have students circle and write four story words that all rhyme (who, blew, through, to). Confirm that rhyming words do not always have the same spelling pattern.

DICTATION REVIEW 16

Materials: pencil, writing paper

Core Words

its	76	now	78	my	80
who	77	people	79		

Review Core Words

of (2), and (3), are (15), they (19), from (23), what (32), their (42), up (50), them (52), many (55), some (56), make (72)

Extra Words

different, country, live, land, names

Have students write the sentences as they are dictated.

1. Many different people make up my country now.
2. Some of them live from its land.
3. Who are they and what are their names?

■ **Follow-Up Activity**

Ask students what it means to live from the land. Ask students if they know people who live from the land or have read about them in stories. Then discuss other ways to make a living. Have students write about what they would like to do to make a living when they are grown.

REVIEW 17 Core Words 81–85

Use after Core Word 85

CLOZE STORY REVIEW 17

Materials: Master 17, pencil, writing paper

Core Words

made	81	did	83	only	85
over	82	down	84		

Review Core Words

many (55), would (59), could (70), than (73), its (76)

Tell students this is a story about a bright star in the night sky. Review *then* and *than, its* and *it's*. Read the story as students write the words. Then have students write their answers to the story questions.

Make a Wish

Day was almost (1) <u>over</u>. Soon the night sky (2) <u>would</u> be full of (3) <u>many</u> bright stars shining (4) <u>down</u> on me. Now I (5) <u>could</u> see (6) <u>only</u> one star. It was the first star. (7) <u>Its</u> twinkle was brighter (8) <u>than</u> any star I had ever seen. I fixed my eyes upon it and I (9) <u>made</u> a wish. Have you ever wished upon a star? (10) <u>Did</u> your wish come true?

■ Extend Learning

1. Have students share their answers to the story questions. Then review this poem by writing it on the chalkboard as students predict the spellings: "Star light, star bright, / First star I see tonight, / I wish I may, I wish I might, / Have the wish I wish tonight." Have students form small groups to read the poem aloud. Share *Star of Fear, Star of Hope* by Jo Hoestlandt, a book that recalls the old rhyme "Stars at morning, better take warning. / Stars at night, hope is in sight" and relates it to the story of an old woman's memory of the Nazi occupation of France that is appropriate for a young audience.

2. Have students circle and write the story word antonyms *day* and *night*. Then have them identify other story words for which they can name an antonym. Choices may include *full/empty, down/up, first/last, true/false.*

3. Have students circle and write the rhyming story words *night* and *bright, would* and *could*. Then have them identify other story words for which they can write a rhyming word. Choices may include *wish/fish, down/town, day/pay, star/far, did/kid.*

4. Have students circle and write the story words *almost, many, only.* Help students identify a word that could be used in the place of each of these words in the story, but not change the meaning. Choices may include *nearly, several, just.*

DICTATION REVIEW 17

Materials: pencil, writing paper

Core Words

made	81	did	83	only	85
over	82	down	84		

Review Core Words

the (1), of (2), a (4), one (28), had (29), what (32), when (35), these (58), who (77)

Extra Words

mouse, run, clock, cake, jumped, moon, Mary

Have students write the sentences as they are dictated.

1. When did the mouse run down the clock? (after it struck one—Hickory, Dickory, Dock)
2. Who made a cake? (the baker's man—Pat-a-Cake)
3. What jumped over the moon? (the cow—Hey, Diddle, Diddle)
4. Mary had only one of these. (a lamb—Mary Had a Little Lamb)

■ Follow-Up Activity

Have students find and write a response to each sentence request. Then discuss the students' responses.

REVIEW 18 Core Words 86–90

Use after Core Word 90

CLOZE STORY REVIEW 18

Materials: Master 18, pencil, writing paper

Core Words

way	86	use	88	water	90
find	87	may	89		

Review Core Words

but (31), there (37), their (42), more (63), make (72), its (76), people (79)

Tell students this is a guessing-game story. Review *there* and *their, its* and *it's*. Read the story as students write the words. Remind students that titles are capitalized. Then have students write the title word.

---

(1) Water

You can (2) find this up in a cloud or see it in the sea. It can (3) make power for our electric lights. (4) People might (5) use it when they are thirsty or when they clean (6) their dog. It (7) may disappear if you heat it, (8) but if you freeze it, it takes up (9) more space. Sometimes (10) there is too much or too little of it. Either (11) way, it's a problem for us. (12) Its name begins with w.

■ **Extend Learning**

1. Discuss the information in the story. Ask students to write or tell: What is water power? What is steam? How could you prove that frozen water takes up more space when it freezes? What problems arise when there is too much or too little water?

2. Have students circle and write the story words *there, their, it's, its, are, our.* Contrast each pair of words. Have students work in pairs to write sentences using the words.

3. Have students circle and write the story words *use* and *us.* Contrast the two. Have students write sentences using the words.

4. Introduce *Splish Splash: Poems* by Joan Bransfield Graham for primary poems about water in all its forms. Have students choose their favorite poem and write reasons for why they like it best.

5. Have students circle and write the story words *can, might, may, space, way.* Discuss the meaning of the words in the story. Then discuss another meaning for each of the words. Help students identify other words that have more than one meaning.

DICTATION REVIEW 18

Materials: pencil, writing paper

Core Words

way	86	use	88	water	90
find	87	may	89		

Review Core Words

of (2), in (6), you (8), it (10), be (21), what (32), all (33), how (49), out (51), many (55), some (56), more (63), time(s) (69), than (73)

Extra Words

us, need, today, think

Have students write the sentences as they are dictated.

1. All of us use water in some way.
2. Find out how many times you need some today.
3. It may be more than what you think.

■ **Follow-Up Activity**

Have students list ways they used water in one day.

REVIEW 19 — Core Words 91–95

Use after Core Word 95

CLOZE STORY REVIEW 19

Materials: Master 19, pencil, writing paper

Core Words

long	91	very	93	word(s)	95
little	92	after	94		

Review Core Words

with (17), each (47), about (48), many (55), first (74), people (79), down (84)

Tell students that this is a story that tells how to play a good game. Read the story as students write the words. Then have them follow the story directions to play the Name Game.

Name Game

Here's a game for you. Write your (1) first name in (2) very big capital letters (3) down the side of your paper. (4) After every letter, write two (5) words that tell something (6) about you. (7) Each one must begin (8) with that letter of your name. If you have a (9) long name, you must think of (10) many ways to describe yourself. (11) People with short names will have a (12) little less to do.

■ Extend Learning

1. Have students show and tell their Name Game. Then have students work in pairs to choose the name of a celebrity and play the Name Game with his or her name. Provide time to share the results.
2. Have students circle and write the story word *for.* Ask them to write its number word homophone (four). Contrast the words. Then discuss the other number homophones and their partners *one/won, two/to/too, eight/ate.*
3. Have students write the words in the story title. Then write more words that follow this rhyming spelling pattern. Choices may include *blame, came, dame, fame, flame, frame, lame, mame, same, shame, tame.* Discuss any unfamiliar words.
4. Have students circle the review story words *you, your, of, have, with.* Then have students write the words in alphabetical order.

DICTATION REVIEW 19

Materials: pencil, writing paper

Core Words

long	91	very	93	word(s)	95
little	92	after	94		

Review Core Words

the (1), a (4), in (6), you (8), that (9), from (23), or (26), one (28), then (53), many (55), make (72), its (76), made (81), use (88)

Extra Words

write, big, letters, story

Have students write the sentences as they are dictated. Provide assistance with the comma in the third sentence.
1. Write one very long word.
2. Then make many big or little words from its letters.
3. After that, use the words you made in a story.

■ Follow-Up Activity

Have students complete the activity requested in the sentences. Provide time for sharing the words and stories. Repeat the make-more-words activity in cooperative groups in which all groups begin working with the same long word. Time the activity (about 5 minutes). Share the words.

REVIEW 20 Core Words 96–100

Use after Core Word 100

CLOZE STORY REVIEW 20

Materials: Master 20, pencil, old magazines, scissors, paste, heavy paper

Core Words

called	96	where	98	know	100
just	97	most	99		

Review Core Words

from (23), your (40), out (51), then (53), than (73), little (92), after (94)

Tell students that this is a story that tells how to make something fun. Read the story as students write the words. Then have them follow the story directions to create their puzzle.

Puzzle Fun

First, find a place to work (1) <u>where</u> you can cut and paste. Choose the picture you like (2) <u>most</u> of all (3) <u>from</u> an old magazine. Cut (4) <u>out</u> the picture. (5) <u>Then</u> paste it on heavy paper that is a (6) <u>little</u> larger (7) <u>than</u> the picture. (8) <u>After</u> the paste dries, cut the picture into pieces. Do you (9) <u>know</u> what you (10) <u>just</u> made? It's (11) <u>called</u> a puzzle! Can you put (12) <u>your</u> puzzle together?

■ Extend Learning

1. Have students exchange puzzles and try to put the new puzzle together.
2. Have students circle and write the story words *then* and *than.* Contrast the words. Have students write a sentence using the words.
3. Have students circle and write the story words *first, work, old, out, little, after.* Next to each word, ask students to write its antonym. Later, put the answers on the chalkboard so that students can check their answers and proofread their spellings.
4. Write *puzzle* on the chalkboard and underline the *le.* Have students circle and write a story word that ends in the same sound and letters (little). Then have students find and write more *le* words, such as *people, table, circle, bicycle, title.*
5. Have students circle the story word *old.* Then have them add beginning letters to make new words. Have them repeat the activity with the story word *all.*

DICTATION REVIEW 20

Materials: pencil, writing paper

Core Words

called	96	where	98	know	100
just	97	most	99		

Review Core Words

the (1), of (2), for (12), are (15), they (19),
one (28), all (33), we (36), will (46), time (69),
no (71), now (78), find (87)

Extra Words

four, us, our, hiding, place

Have students write the sentences as they are dictated.
1. They just called for all four of us.
2. Most of the time they find our hiding place.
3. No one will know where we are now.

■ Follow-Up Activity

Have students write about a good hiding place and
tell why it's such a good one.

REVIEW 21 — Core Words 101–105

Use after Core Word 105

CLOZE STORY REVIEW 21

Materials: Master 21, pencil, writing paper

Core Words

get	101	back	103	go	105
through	102	much	104		

Review Core Words

from (23), have (25), which (41), been (75),
now (78), little (92), called (96)

Tell students that this is a story about a silly chicken
they may know. Read the story as students write the
words. Then have students write their answer to the
story question.

The Sky is Falling

Once a small acorn fell (1) <u>from</u> an oak tree. It
came down (2) <u>through</u> the air and hit Chicken
(3) <u>Little</u> on the (4) <u>back</u> of her head. (5) <u>Now</u> this
chicken did not always use very (6) <u>much</u> good
sense. She (7) <u>called</u> to her friends, "The sky is
falling! It struck me! (8) <u>Get</u> help! (9) <u>Go</u> tell the
king!" If it had (10) <u>been</u> you on (11) <u>which</u> this
tiny acorn fell, what would you (12) <u>have</u> done?

■ Extend Learning

1. Have students share their answer to the story
   question. Review the story of Chicken Little.
   Share with students different versions of the old
   tale. Choices may include Steven Kellogg's
   Chicken Little, Gavin Bishop's *Chicken Licken*,
   and Paul Galdone's *Henny Penny*. Contrast one
   element in the stories, such as the major
   characters.
2. Have students find and write the story words *small,
   fell, hit.* Then have them find words or phrases in the
   story that have nearly the same meaning (tiny/little,
   came down through the air and hit/struck).
3. Have students circle and write story word
   homophones, such as *through, not, sense, to,
   would.* Then identify and discuss their
   homophone counterparts.
4. Write *fall* on the chalkboard. Then have students
   circle its other word forms in the story (falling, fell).
5. Have students tell in writing about a character
   from another story who did not use good sense.

DICTATION REVIEW 21

Materials: pencil, writing paper

Core Words

get	101	back	103	go	105
through	102	much	104		

Review Core Words

to (5), that (9), he (11), for (12), was (13),
with (17), his (18), at (20), had (29), there (37),
said (43), do (45), will (46), so (57), two (65),
him (67), see (68), first (74)

Extra Words

wanted, friends, Dad, work, got, help, home

Have students write the sentences as they are dictated.

1. Will wanted to go see his two friends.
2. Dad said that he had to get through with his work first.
3. So Will got back to work.
4. There was much for him to do to help at home.

■ Follow-Up Activity

Discuss the kind of work Will may have been asked to finish. Then have students tell in writing about the work they do to help at home.

REVIEW 22 Core Words 106–110

Use after Core Word 110

CLOZE STORY REVIEW 22

Materials: Master 22, pencil, writing paper

Core Words

good 106	write 108	me 110
new 107	our 109	

Review Core Words

as (16), they (19), when (35), like (66), people (79), use (88), words (95)

Tell students that this is a story that tells about words that are tricky to spell. Read the story as students write the words. Then have students explain in writing why homophones may create a spelling problem.

Spelling Homophones

Help (1) <u>me</u>! I'm a (2) <u>good</u> speller, except for (3) <u>when</u> I (4) <u>use</u> homophones. These (5) <u>words</u> sound alike, but (6) <u>they</u> have different letters and meanings. For example, if you're writing "in an hour," *hour* isn't spelled (7) <u>like</u> "(8) <u>our</u> class." Or if you're writing "knew the answer," *knew* is not spelled the same (9) <u>as</u> "a (10) <u>new</u> coat." Do (11) <u>people</u> ever learn to (12) <u>write</u> the right letters?

■ Extend Learning

1. Discuss the last sentence in the story, focusing on *write/right.* Have students share their written explanations. Help students create context-sentence references for the homophones that challenge them most.

2. Have students find and write story homophones, such as *or, for, not, do, to, write, right, new, knew, our, hour.* Then identify and discuss their homophone counterparts. Include a discussion of *too,* as it will be a Core Word soon.

3. Have students circle and write the story word contractions (I'm, you're, isn't). Then have them write the words that make up each contraction. Have students find and write more contractions.

4. Have students circle and write the story words *write* and *writing.* Review the rule for adding the *ing* suffix to words that end in silent *e.* Then have students write the review words *have, time, make, like, use.* Have students add *ing* to each of these words.

5. Write *spell* on the chalkboard. Then have students circle and write its other word forms found in the story (spelling, speller, spelled).

DICTATION REVIEW 22

Materials: pencil, writing paper

Core Words

good 106	write 108	me 110
new 107	our 109	

Review Core Words

a (4), are (15), one (28), all (33), we (36), about (48), many (55), these (58), time (69), made (81), little (92), very (93), just (97)

Extra Words

class, book(s), small, wrote

Have students write the sentences as they are dictated.

1. Our class just made a new little book.
2. We write many small books.
3. These books are very good.
4. One time we all wrote a book about me.

■ Follow-Up Activity

Have students tell in writing about their favorite student-made or class-made book. Have them give reasons why it is their favorite.

REVIEW 23 — Core Words 111–115

Use after Core Word 115

CLOZE STORY REVIEW 23

Materials: Master 23, pencil, writing paper

Core Words

man	111	any	113	same	115
too	112	day	114		

Review Core Words

to (5), that (9), have (25), then (53), two (65), know (100), write (108)

Tell students that this is a story about spelling. Review *to, two,* and *too.* Read the story as students write the words. Then have them write their answers to the story questions.

More Than One

(1) <u>To</u> spell the word (2) <u>that</u> means more than one (3) <u>day</u>, you just (4) <u>write</u> an *s* at the end of the word. It works the (5) <u>same</u> way with almost (6) <u>any</u> word. One dog is spelled *dog,* but (7) <u>two</u> of them becomes *dogs.* One book is *book,* but if you (8) <u>have</u> four of them it is *books.* Is this (9) <u>too</u> easy for you? Well (10) <u>then</u>, do you (11) <u>know</u> the spelling for *more than one* (12) <u>man</u>?

■ Extend Learning

1. Have students share their answers to the story questions. Create a list of other irregular plurals on the chalkboard, such as *woman/women, child/children, mouse/mice.* Have students predict the spellings of the words as they are written.

2. Have students circle and write the story words *one, to, two, too, for, four.* Discuss these homophones and their use, including *won.* Then have students circle and write more story word homophones, such as *write, way, know.* Have them write their homophone partners.

3. Have students circle and write the story words *then, than, them.* Contrast the words. Have students write the words in sentences.

4. Have students circle and write the story word *know.* Then have them write words they find inside of *know* (no, now). Have them repeat this activity with other story words.

5. Have students predict the spellings through the word preview procedure of the review story words *word, more, than, them* and the new story words *dog, book, spell, spelling.* Have students check their predictions against the spelling of the story words.

DICTATION REVIEW 23

Materials: pencil, writing paper

Core Words

man	111	any	113	same	115
too	112	day	114		

Review Core Words

the (1), a (4), you (8), that (9), it (10), he (11), was (13), as (16), his (18), this (22), one (28), not (30), said (43), long (91), called (96), just (97), know (100), new (107)

Extra Words

once, name, himself, another

Have students write the sentences as they are dictated.
1. A man once said that his name was too long.
2. One day he called himself another name.
3. It was not just any name.
4. This new name was the same as a name you know.

■ Follow-Up Activity

Ask students to write the famous name they think this man may have chosen for his own. Share the varied answers. Then have students tell in writing about a name they'd like to have instead of their own. Have them give reasons why they'd like the new name.

REVIEW 24 — Core Words 116–120

Use after Core Word 120

CLOZE STORY REVIEW 24

Materials: Master 24, pencil, writing paper

Core Words

right	116	think	118	around	120
look	117	also	119		

Review Core Words

of (2), as (16), were (34), there (37), their (42), these (58), through (102)

Tell students that this is a story about an exciting parade through the city streets. Read the story as students write the words. Than have students write what they like best in a parade.

The Parade is Coming!

They (1) <u>were</u> all sitting down along the edge (2) <u>of</u> the street waiting for the parade to come by. "(3) <u>Look</u>! Listen!" called one of them. "I (4) <u>think</u> I hear it!" Soon (5) <u>there</u> was music all (6) <u>around</u> them (7) <u>as</u> the band came marching (8) <u>through</u>. Can you see (9) <u>these</u> marchers? (10) <u>Their</u> feet are stepping to the beat—left, (11) <u>right</u>, left. Can you (12) <u>also</u> hear the big drums?

■ Extend Learning

1. Have students share their written answer, telling what they like best in a parade. Ask students to visualize a parade. Then tell what they see and hear in their parade. List the things on the chalkboard. Ask students to predict the spellings of the words as they are written.

2. Have students find and write the story word homophones. Choices may include *for, to, by, one, hear, there/their, through, right, see, beat.* Then have students write their homophone partners. Discuss the meanings of the homophones. Then have students write selected homophones in sentences.

3. Write *march* on the chalkboard. Then have students circle and write the story word *marching*. Next, write these words on the chalkboard and ask students to write the words with the *ing* suffix: *come, sit, wait, call, step, hear, beat.* Discuss the spelling rules that apply.

4. Write the story word *listen* on the chalkboard. Discuss the silent *t*. Have students circle and write more story words that have silent letters. Choices may include *through, right, parade, edge, come.*

DICTATION REVIEW 24

Materials: pencil, writing paper

Core Words

right	116	think	118	around	120
look	117	also	119		

Review Core Words

the (1), and (3), to (5), you (8), one (28), your (40), then (53), more (63), time (69), only (85), may (89), back (103), go (105), any (113)

Extra Words

before, cross, street, left

Have students write the sentences as they are dictated.
1. Think before you cross any street.
2. Look to your left and also to your right.
3. Look back around to the left one more time.
4. Only then may you go.

■ Follow-Up Activity

Ask students to contrast two street crossings—one with signals and one without. Have them tell in writing how the two require different skills for the walker, or pedestrian.

REVIEW 25　Core Words 121–125

Use after Core Word 125

CLOZE STORY REVIEW 25

Materials: Master 25, pencil, writing paper

Core Words

another	121	come	123	three	125
came	122	work	124		

Review Core Words

was (13), what (32), there (37), then (53), many (55), first (74), little (92)

Tell students that this is a story about three familiar animals and their enemy, the sly wolf. Read the story as students write the words. Then have students write their answer to the story question.

Three Pigs and a Wolf

The (1) <u>first</u> pig did not (2) <u>work</u> long to build his straw house. It would (3) <u>come</u> down with a huff and a puff. (4) <u>There</u> was (5) <u>another</u> pig who used (6) <u>little</u> sticks to make his place. The third pig took (7) <u>many</u> days to construct his home of strong bricks. (8) <u>Then</u> along (9) <u>came</u> a hungry wolf. He looked at the (10) <u>three</u> homes. (11) <u>What</u> do you suppose this wolf (12) <u>was</u> thinking?

■ Extend Learning

1. Have students share their answer to the story question. Then ask students to take turns retelling a part of this familiar tale. Discuss the moral of the story.
2. Write *build*, *make*, and *construct* on the chalkboard. Have students circle the words in the story. Discuss their synonyms. Repeat the activity with *house*, *place*, *home*.
3. Have students circle and write the story words *come* and *came*. Note that all but one of the letters are the same. Then have them circle and write the review story words *his*, *would*, *down*. By changing just one letter in each of these words, have students write a new word.
4. Have students circle the story words *huff* and *puff*. Then have them find and write more story words that rhyme, such as *long/strong*, *you/to/who/do*, *he/three*.
5. Have students work in pairs to list story titles for tales that feature a wolf. For each correctly spelled title, award one point. Students should be allowed to use spelling references.

DICTATION REVIEW 25

Materials: writing paper, pencil

Core Words

another	121	come	123	three	125
came	122	work	124		

Review Core Words

of (2), a (4), to (5), had (29), all (33), we (36), time (69), my (80), over (82), did (83), very (93), most (99), good (106), our (109), too (112), also (119)

Extra Words

friend, house, wanted, us, school

Have students write the sentences as they are dictated. Provide assistance with the comma in the second sentence.

1. My friend came over to our house.
2. Another friend wanted to come, too.
3. All three of us did most of our school work.
4. We also had a very good time.

■ Follow-Up Activity

Ask students to write three good things and three bad things about doing homework with a group of friends.

REVIEW 26 · Core Words 126-130

Use after Core Word 130

CLOZE STORY REVIEW 26

Materials: Master 26, pencil, writing paper

Core Words

must	126	does	128	even	130
because	127	part	129		

Review Core Words

your (40), their (42), these (58), people (79), through (102), much (104), also (119)

Tell students that this is a story about a family that works together to make a living. Read the story as students write the words. Then have students write their answer to the story question.

Making Things to Make a Living

The family works (1) <u>through</u> the day and (2) <u>even</u> after dark (3) <u>because</u> they (4) <u>must</u> make things for the market. They grow (5) <u>much</u> food. The (6) <u>part</u> they don't eat goes to the market. They (7) <u>also</u> make new brooms, candles, and mittens for (8) <u>people</u>. At the fall market, they sell or trade all (9) <u>these</u> good things to make (10) <u>their</u> living. How (11) <u>does</u> (12) <u>your</u> family make a living?

■ Extend Learning

1. Have students share their answer to the story question. Then introduce the Caldecott award book *Ox-Cart Man*, by Donald Hall and illustrated by Barbara Cooney. The family in this superb picture book creates goods for market as described in this story.

2. Have students circle and write the story words *their* and *through*. Discuss the words and their homophone partners. Then ask students to write *their* and *there*, *through* and *threw* in sentences to differentiate the homophones.

3. Have students circle and write the story words *must* and *much*. Contrast their spellings. Have students write the words in sentences.

4. Write the story word *market* on the chalkboard. The clipped word *mart* is often used in its place. Provide another example: *bicycle, bike*. Then have students find and write the longer forms of clipped words, such as *math, gym, champ, burger, flu, gas, limo, phone*.

DICTATION REVIEW 26

Materials: pencil, writing paper

Core Words

must	126	does	128	even	130
because	127	part(s)	129		

Review Core Words

of (2), a (4), to (5), is (7), are (15), as (16), they (19), this (22), not (30), all (33), there (37), their (42), how (49), many (55), some (56), so (57), people (79), words (95), know (100), good (106), also (119)

Extra Words

spell (er, ed, ing), sound, always, check

Have students write the sentences as they are dictated. Provide assistance with the comma in the third sentence.

1. Even a good speller does not know how to spell all words.

2. This is because there are so many words.

3. Also, parts of some words are not spelled as they sound.

4. People must always check their spelling.

■ Follow-Up Activity

Discuss spelling resources available in the classroom for a writer. Then have students tell in writing why they think good spelling is important.

REVIEW 27 Core Words 131–135

Use after Core Word 135

CLOZE STORY REVIEW 27

Materials: Master 27, pencil, writing paper

Core Words

place	131	such	133	take	135
well	132	here	134		

Review Core Words

each (47), more (63), water (90), around (120), three (125), must (126), even (130)

Tell students that this is a story about how they can make music in an unusual way. Read the story as students write the words. Then have students choose a favorite musical instrument and describe in writing the kind of music it makes.

Musical Glasses

You can make a musical instrument with things you find (1) <u>around</u> the house. It is (2) <u>such</u> an easy thing to do. (3) <u>Here</u> is how. (4) <u>Place</u> (5) <u>three</u> drinking glasses in a row and fill (6) <u>each</u> with a different amount of (7) <u>water</u>. To play, you (8) <u>must</u> tap the glasses with a spoon. Add (9) <u>more</u> glasses for an (10) <u>even</u> better sound. (11) <u>Take</u> time to practice. Soon you will play (12) <u>well</u>.

■ Extend Learning

1. Have students share their written descriptions of the musical sound of an instrument of their choice. Then demonstrate making musical glasses so that students may duplicate the activity at home. Have students take turns playing the musical glasses. Ask them which musical instrument is most like the musical glasses (xylophone). Ask students how to lower the tone of a glass (adding more water to the glass). Ask if plastic glasses, rather than glass ones, would be able to make music (no).

2. Share with students the picture book *The Philharmonic Gets Dressed* by Karla Kuskin. Have students make a list of the musical instruments pictured in this book.

3. Ask students to circle and write the story word *such*. Then have them write *much*. Repeat the activity with *here/there, place/face, three/tree, row/grow, each/peach, spoon/soon, sound/found, take/bake, well/bell*.

4. Have students circle and write the story word *three*. Then have students write more number words.

DICTATION REVIEW 27

Materials: pencil, writing paper

Core Words

place	131	such	133	take	135
well	132	here	134		

Review Core Words

and (3), a (4), is (7), you (8), I (24), one (28), your (40), do (45), will (46), how (49), some (56), into (61), my (80), little (92), know (100), good (106), new (107), look (117), think (118), come (123)

Extra Words

color(s), blue, paint, yellow

Have students write the sentences as they are dictated.
1. How well do you know your colors?
2. I will place a little blue paint into some yellow.
3. Come here and take a look.
4. I think my new color is such a good one.

■ Follow-Up Activity

Ask students to tell in writing what color was made (green). If necessary, demonstrate with food color or paint. Then have students list things that are green.

REVIEW 28   Core Words 136–140

Use after Core Word 140

CLOZE STORY REVIEW 28

Materials: Master 28, pencil, writing paper

Core Words

why	136	put	138	away	140
help	137	different	139		

Review Core Words

there (37), about (48), find (87), words (95), too (112), think (118), because (127)

Tell students this is a story about the parts of some books. Read the story as students write the words. Then have students write their answer to the story question.

Finding Information in a Book

(1) There is a way to easily (2) find information in a book. The table of contents lists the (3) different chapters. (4) Put (5) away the big dictionary (6) because the book's glossary tells the meanings of important (7) words. The index can (8) help you, (9) too. It lists the pages that tell (10) about a topic. (11) Why do you (12) think the glossary and index are in alphabetical order?

■ Extend Learning

1. Have students share their answer to the story question. Have students explore books to find the table of contents, glossary, and index. Using a book that all students have, identify specific information and have students see how quickly they can find it using these resources. Point out the guide words in the glossary and have students explain how they can help the user.

2. Have students circle and write the story words *a way* and *away*. Contrast the two. Expand the lesson to *may be* and *maybe*. Then have students write the words in sentences.

3. Have students circle and write the story word *help*. Then explain how the words *aid, assist, serve,* and *support* mean nearly the same thing.

4. Have students circle and write the story words *to, too, there*. Then have students write their homophone partners. Have students write the homophones in sentences. Then have them check their homophone sentences with a partner to determine the accuracy of their use.

DICTATION REVIEW 28

Materials: pencil, writing paper

Core Words

why	136	put	138	away	140
help	137	different	139		

Review Core Words

the (1), a (4), to (5), is (7), it (10), he (11),
be (21), from (23), one (28), what (32), we (36),
there (37), if (44), would (59), other(s) (60),
him (67), way (86), little (92), back (103),
think(s) (118), because (127), does (128)

Extra Words

duck, stay, happy, happen

Have students write the sentences as they are dictated.
1. Why does one little duck stay away from the others?
2. It is because he thinks he is different.
3. Is there a way to help him be happy?
4. What would happen if we put him back?

■ Follow-Up Activity

Ask students to identify a story in which one duck felt he was different from the other ducks (The Ugly Duckling). Discuss answers to the sentence questions. Have students tell in writing how this story ended.

REVIEW 29 Core Words 141-145

Use after Core Word 145

CLOZE STORY REVIEW 29

Materials: Master 29, pencil, writing paper

Core Words

again	141	went	143	number	145
off	142	old	144		

Review Core Words

when (35), time (69), where (98), new (107),
our (109), take (135), why (136)

Tell students that this is a story that tells ways a map can be a big help. Read the story as students write the words. Then have students write why these travelers had a road map that looked old at the end of their trip.

Using a Map

(1) When we (2) went on a car trip, we did not start (3) off without (4) our map. (5) Why did we (6) take a map? A map can be a big help! The map told us (7) where the mountains and lakes were. It showed us the (8) number of miles between cities. We looked at the map over and over (9) again. By the (10) time we got home, we had (11) new memories, but a map that looked (12) old!

■ Extend Learning

1. Have students share their written explanations for the old-looking road map. Have students explore road maps to determine how to use a map for a car trip. Identify the symbols and point out use of the map key. Have students form small groups to "read" their maps. Then have each group plan and record a short car trip route, including what they will see along the way.

2. Have students circle and write the story antonyms *new* and *old*. Have them circle and write the story words *start, off, without, take, big*. Then have students write an antonym for each.

3. Have students circle and write the story word *help*. Then have students write other word forms for *help*. Choices may include *helped, helps, helping, helpless, helplessly, helpful, helpfully*. Repeat the activity with other story words for which the other word forms need reinforcement.

4. Have students circle and write the story words that begin with *wh* (when, why, where). Then have students find and write more words that begin with *wh*.

5. Have students find and circle story words that follow the *long-vowel-final-silent e* pattern (take, lakes, miles, time, home).

DICTATION REVIEW 29

Materials: pencil, writing paper

Core Words

again	141	went	143	number	145
off	142	old	144		

Review Core Words

the (1), of (2), and (3), a (4), to (5), is (7), it (10), on (14), they (19), be (21), this (22), from (23), I (24), time(s) (69), did (83), may (89), very (93), get (101), go (105), think (118), another (121), because (127), does (128), why (136)

Extra Words

reading, light, today, store

Have students write the sentences as they are dictated.
1. Why does this reading light go off and on again?
2. It did it a number of times today.
3. I think it may be because it is very old.
4. They went to get another light from the store.

■ Follow-Up Activity

Ask students to tell in writing about something that caused a problem for them because it was old and not working well. Then have them write about something that was new, but did not work well.

REVIEW 30 | Core Words 146–150
Use after Core Word 150

CLOZE STORY REVIEW 30

Materials: Master 30, pencil, writing paper

Core Words

great 146	men 148	small 150
tell 147	say 149	

Review Core Words

their (42), would (59), most (99), through (102), think (118), around (120), different (139)

Tell students that this is a story that tells about an unusual dentist. Read the story as students write the words. Then have students write their answer to the story question.

The Dentist

Doctor De Soto is a (1) great dentist known (2) around the world. All his patients (3) think that he is the best and (4) tell about the times he fixed (5) their teeth. Now, (6) most dentists are (7) men or women. But Doctor De Soto is (8) different. He is a (9) small mouse. What (10) would you (11) say to him if he walked (12) through the door to help you as you sat waiting in his dental chair?

■ Extend Learning

1. Have students share their answer to the story question. Then share William Steig's *Doctor De Soto* (1983 Newbery Honor Book) or its sequel, *Doctor De Soto Goes to Africa*. These stories feature the great mouse dentist. Then have students write their own De Soto sequel story.

2. Have students circle and write the story words *tell, all, small*. Have students write the review words *will, called, well*. Note the double letter *l*. Then have them find and write more words with the double *l*. Expand the lesson to other story words with double letters (teeth, different, door).

3. Have students circle and write the story words *their, would, through*. Contrast them with their homophones. Then have students write the homophones in sentences.

4. Have students circle and write the story word *Doctor*. Discuss why it is capitalized. Write its abbreviation on the chalkboard, *Dr.* Then discuss other titles and their abbreviations, such as *Mr., Mrs., Ms.*

DICTATION REVIEW 30

Materials: pencil, writing paper

Core Words

great 146	men 148	small 150
tell 147	say 149	

Review Core Words

the (1), of (2), and (3), in (6), you (8), are (15), they (19), have (25), all (33), there (37), can (38), their (42), about (48), many (55), some (56), these (58), two (65), people (79), way (86), good (106), help(ed) (137)

Extra Words

women, world, names, us

Have students write the sentences as they are dictated.
1. There are many great men and women in the world.
2. They all have helped in some small way.
3. Can you say their names?
4. Tell us about two of these good people.

■ Follow-Up Activity

Have students write about two men or women who did something great to help others. Have them describe the contributions and give reasons why their help was important.

REVIEW 31 | Core Words 151–155

Use after Core Word 155

CLOZE STORY REVIEW 31

Materials: Master 31, pencil, writing paper

Core Words

every	151	still	153	name	155
found	152	between	154		

Review Words

have (25), when (35), there (37), then (53), where (98), place (131), went (143)

Tell students that this story is about something important that got lost. Read the story as students write the words. Then have students write their answer to the story question, including what they lost, why it was important to them, and if their lost object was ever found.

It's Lost

Mother wrote May's (1) <u>name</u> on her lunch ticket and gave it to her when she (2) <u>went</u> to school. But (3) <u>when</u> May got to school, (4) <u>there</u> was no ticket. She looked, but (5) <u>still</u> her ticket was no (6) <u>place</u> to be (7) <u>found</u>. (8) <u>Where</u> was it? Had she lost it (9) <u>between</u> home and school? (10) <u>Every</u> now and (11) <u>then</u>, things get lost. (12) <u>Have</u> you ever lost something important to you?

■ Extend Learning

1. Have students share their answer to the story question. Then discuss the school's Lost and Found. Have students write predictions of the most common items found there. Then verify their predictions by visiting the Lost and Found. You may wish to start a classroom Lost and Found.
2. Have students circle and write the story words *there* and *where*. Have students circle *here* inside of the words. Then have them write more story words and the words they find inside of them. Share the results.
3. Have students alphabetize the story words they wrote in the story blanks.
4. Have students circle and write the title word *It's*. Discuss why it begins with a capital letter. Discuss the words that comprise the contraction. Then

have students find and write more contractions and write the words that comprise each.
5. Have students predict the spellings through the word preview procedure of the review story words *when, was, now, you* and the new story words *lunch, school, lost, something*. Have students check their predictions against the spelling of the story words.

DICTATION REVIEW 31

Materials: pencil, writing paper

Core Words

every	151	still	153	name	155
found	152	between	154		

Review Core Words

the (1), and (3), a (4), it (10), was (13), they (19), I (24), have (25), not (30), we (36), said (43), two (65), see (68), could (70), did (83), down (84), water (90), look(ed) (117), small (150)

Extra Words

lake, green, hills, clear, fish

Have students write the sentences as they are dictated.
1. The small lake was between two green hills.
2. They said it did not have a name.
3. We found the water still and clear.
4. I looked down and could see every fish.

■ Follow-Up Activity

Have students draw a picture of this small lake and name it. Ask students to list uses for this small lake (irrigation, swimming, fishing, fire protection, etc.).

REVIEW 32 | Core Words 156–160

Use after Core Word 160

CLOZE STORY REVIEW 32

Materials: Master 32, pencil, writing paper

Core Words

should	156	big	158	air	160
home	157	give	159		

Review Words

there (37), their (42), because (127), such (133), different (139), between (154), name (155)

Tell students that this story is about special kinds of trucks. Read the story as students write the words. Then have students write their answer to the story question.

Trucks

(1) There are many (2) different kinds of trucks. Some are (3) big and carry heavy loads, (4) such as large moving vans that transport furniture to your new (5) home. Some are refrigerated to (6) give (7) their loads a cool ride. These trucks may carry ice cream (8) because it (9) should not be in warm (10) air (11) between the dairy and the store. What other special trucks can you (12) name?

■ Extend Learning

1. Have students share their answers to the story question. Discuss trucks and the work they do. Special trucks include fire trucks, armored trucks, campers, garbage trucks, cement mixers, log trucks, dump trucks, pickups, wreckers, and tank trucks.

2. Have students find and circle the story word *transport*. Discuss its meaning. Ask students to think of other words that could be substituted for *transport* in the story. Note a more familiar form of the word, *transportation*. Have students find and circle the story word *refrigerated*. Discuss its meaning. Note a more familiar form of the word, *refrigerator*.

3. Have students circle and write the story word homophones *there* and *their*. Contrast the words. Then have students find more story homophones, such as *some, to, new, not, be*.

4. Have students circle and write the story words *moving* and *ride*. Then have them write *move* and *riding*. Discuss the silent *e* and the addition of the *ing* suffix. Expand the lesson by asking students to add the *ing* suffix to the review words *like, make, write, come, place, take,* and *name*.

DICTATION REVIEW 32

Materials: pencil, writing paper

Core Words

should	156	big	158	air	160
home	157	give	159		

Review Core Words

the (1), and (3), to (5), you (8), with (17), one(s) (28), can (38), these (58), two (65), make (72), use (88), little (92), words (word) (95), know (100), new (107), write (108), another (121), work (124), small (150)

Extra Words

sometimes, homework, short, mail, please

Have students write the sentences as they are dictated.

1. Sometimes you can use little words to write big words.
2. Home and work should give you homework.
3. You know the short words air and mail.
4. Please make another new word with these two small ones.

■ Follow-Up Activity

Have students complete the activity suggested in the sentences. Then have students find and write more compound words that use *home, work, air,* and *mail*. Provide time to share the words.

REVIEW 33 · Core Words 161–165

Use after Core Word 165

CLOZE STORY REVIEW 33

Materials: Master 33, pencil, writing paper

Core Words

line	161	own	163	read	165
set	162	under	164		

Review Words

they (19), there (37), their (42), much (104), even (130), every (151), found (152)

Tell students that this story tells them how to become an artist. Read the story as students write the words. Then have students tell in writing something they would like to learn to draw. Have them tell why they'd like to learn to draw it.

■ Extend Learning

1. Have interested students check out books from the library on drawing. Have students demonstrate to the class how to draw an object they learned to draw using one of their reference books. Note that many artists do not try to make their pictures look real.

2. Write *get set* on the chalkboard. Then ask students to find and circle the expression in the story and explain what they think it means. Expand the lesson to a discussion of *all set, set out, set back, set sail, set off, set in, set fire, set on.*

3. Have students circle and write the story word homophones *there* and *their.* Contrast the words. Then have students find more story homophones, such as *to, real, read, for, flower, be.*

4. Have students circle and write the review story words *are, help, who, make, many, good.* Then have students write the words in alphabetical order.

DICTATION REVIEW 33

Materials: pencil, writing paper

Core Words

line	161	own	163	read	165
set	162	under	164		

Review Core Words

the (1), of (2), a (4), to (5), you (8), it (10), on (14), are (15), I (24), have (25), what (32), all (33), your (40), do (45), them (52), then (53), two (65), first (74), long (91), very (93), words (95), write (108), say (149), name (155)

Extra Words

paper, please, friend, try

Have students write the sentences as they are dictated. Provide assistance with the comma in the third sentence.

1. Are you all set to do what I say?
2. Write your own name on the first line of your paper.
3. Under it, please write two very long words.
4. Then have a friend try to read them to you.

■ Follow-Up Activity

Have students complete the activity suggested in the sentences. Then ask students to share their long words with the class.

REVIEW 34 Core Words 166–170

Use after Core Word 170

CLOZE STORY REVIEW 34

Materials: Master 34, pencil, writing paper

Core Words

last	166	us	168	end	170
never	167	left	169		

Review Words

are (15), but (31), find (87), use (88), know (100), our (109), place (131)

Tell students that this is a story that teaches them the meaning of the big word *eponym.* Read the story as students write the words. Then ask students to research eponyms and write the source of one eponym listed in the story.

■ Extend Learning

1. Discuss the meaning of the story word *origin.* Have students share the origin of the eponym they researched. One resource for eponym word stories is *Guppies in Tuxedos: Funny Eponyms* by Marvin Terban.

2. Have students circle and write the often-confused story words *are* and *our*. Contrast the words. Discuss the homophones *our* and *hour*. Then have students use the three words in sentences to differentiate them.

3. Have students circle and write the story words *left, in, him, end, last*. Then have students write their antonyms.

4. Have students circle and write the story words *us* and *use*. Contrast the words. Then have students explore more words that follow this spelling pattern, such as *can/cane, mad/made, Sam/same, fin/fine, bit/bite, not/note, hop/hope*.

DICTATION REVIEW 34

Materials: pencil, writing paper

Core Words

last	166	us	168	end	170
never	167	left	169		

Review Core Words

the (1), to (5), is (7), that (9), it (10), was (13), with (17), this (22), I (24), we (36), would (59), its (76), very (93), right (116), come (123), because (127), away (140), again (141), great (146), big (158), read (165)

Extra Words

story, smiles, hoped, want, hear

Have students write the sentences as they are dictated.
1. The last story we read was great.
2. This is because it left us with very big smiles.
3. We hoped that its end would never come.
4. I want to hear it again right away.

■ Follow-Up Activity

Have students write which story they think this could be. Ask them to tell why the story was a great one.

REVIEW 35 Core Words 171–175

Use after Core Word 175

CLOZE STORY REVIEW 35

Materials: Master 35, pencil, writing paper

Core Words

along	171	might	173	sound	175
while	172	next	174		

Review Words

would (59), little (92), think (118), because (127), help (137), great (146), small (150)

Tell students that this story about a big, strong animal and a very tiny one may be familiar to them. Read the story as students write the words. Then have students write their answer to the story question.

The Lion and the Mouse

(1) <u>While</u> the lion was asleep, a (2) <u>small</u> mouse ran (3) <u>along</u> his nose. This awoke the lion and he seized the tiny mouse. Mouse was afraid (4) <u>because</u> he thought the lion (5) <u>would</u> eat him. (6) <u>Next</u>, in a squeaky (7) <u>sound</u> the mouse pleaded, "Oh, (8) <u>great</u> lion, do not harm me for I promise to (9) <u>help</u> you one day." How do you (10) <u>think</u> a (11) <u>little</u> mouse (12) <u>might</u> aid this big lion?

■ Extend Learning

1. Have students share their answer to the story question. Ask students to find books that recount the "Lion and Mouse" fable. Compare and contrast the versions. Ask students to write the lesson learned.

2. Have students circle and write the story words *harm, seized, pleaded*. Discuss their meaning. Have students brainstorm for synonyms for these words. Then have students try reading the story, substituting the synonyms for the original story words.

3. Have students circle and write the story word *help*. Then have them find a word in the story that means nearly the same thing (aid). Repeat the activity with *small* (tiny, little). Then have students find and write more synonyms for *small*. Choices may include *minute, petite, slight, mini, wee*. Extend the synonym lesson to finding synonyms for the story word *big*.

4. Have students circle and write the story words *small, sound, think,* and *might*. Then have students list words that follow these spelling patterns. Choices may include *tall, fall, wall, call/round, found, hound, pound/blink, drink, pink, sink/sight, right, light, bright*.

DICTATION REVIEW 35

Materials: pencil, writing paper

Core Words

along 171	might 173	sound 175
while 172	next 174	

Review Core Words

of (2), a (4), to (5), in (6), was (13), they (19),
be (21), what (32), all (33), were (34), there (37),
their (42), them (52), then (53), go (105),
right (116), away (140), still (153), should (156),
home (157), line (161)

Extra Words

stood, funny, feet, side

Have students write the sentences as they are dictated.

1. They stood still while they were in line.
2. Then there was a funny sound next to their feet.
3. What might be along side of them?
4. Should they all go home right away?

■ Follow-Up Activity

Have students write what happened next. Then have students share their answers.

REVIEW 36 Core Words 176–180

Use after Core Word 180

CLOZE STORY REVIEW 36

Materials: Master 36, pencil, writing paper

Core Words

below 176	something 178	both 180
saw 177	thought 179	

Review Words

from (23), there (37), said (43), could (70),
first (74), back (103), right (116), between (154),
never (167)

Tell students that this is a story about a famous bridge in California. Read the story as students write the words. Discuss other instances when people said something could not and should not be done. Then when it *was* done, the people changed their minds. Have students write about one of these times.

The Golden Gate Bridge

   Joseph Strauss built (1) <u>something</u> that people (2) <u>both</u> know and love today. In the 1920's, he (3) <u>saw</u> the need for a bridge (4) <u>between</u> San Francisco and the land north of (5) <u>there</u>. He (6) <u>thought</u> it would help people get to and (7) <u>from</u> the city, as well as add a fine structure to the area. But (8) <u>back</u> then, others (9) <u>said</u> Strauss wasn't (10) <u>right</u>. (11) <u>First</u>, no one (12) <u>could</u> ever build a bridge across the water (13) <u>below</u>. Second, such a bridge would (14) <u>never</u> look beautiful.

■ Extend Learning

1. Have students share their writing. Identify on a map the location of the Golden Gate Bridge north of San Francisco. Joseph Strauss pioneered this famous bridge and was its chief engineer. The bridge opened in 1937. Primary students may enjoy *Bridges* by Ken Robbins.

2. Have students circle and write the story words that can have more than one meaning. Choices may include *saw, well, fine, back, right, land.* Discuss the different meanings.

3. Have students circle and write the story words *below* and *between*. Then have them find and write more *be___* words. Choices may include *behind, before, because, become, became, believe, beyond.*

4. Have students circle and write the story words *first* and *second*. Then have them continue to write words in this series—*third, fourth, fifth,* etc.

DICTATION REVIEW 36

Materials: pencil, writing paper

Core Words

below 176	something 178	both 180
saw 177	thought 179	

Review Core Words

the (1), of (2), to (5), in (6), they (19), have (25),
what (32), were (34), we (36), there (37), can (38),
will (46), would (59), see (68), water (90), just (97),
our (109), too (112), come (123), tell (147),
never (167), us (168)

Extra Words

today, important, friends, river

Have students write the sentences as they are dictated. Provide assistance with the comma in the last sentence.

1. We never thought we would see what we saw today.
2. There they were just below us in the water!
3. Both of us will have something important to tell our friends.
4. They can come to the river to see, too.

■ Follow-Up Activity

Have students tell in writing what they think might have been in the water.

REVIEW 37 | Core Words 181–185

Use after Core Word 185

CLOZE STORY REVIEW 37

Materials: Master 37, pencil, writing paper

Core Words

few	181	always	183	large	185
those	182	show	184		

Review Words

there (37), their (42), about (48), out (51), too (112), because (127), found (152), read (165), might (173)

Tell students that this is a story about very large beasts no longer alive today. Read the story as students write the words. Then have students write their answer to the story question.

The Disappearing Dinosaurs

I've (1) always wanted to know why all the (2) large dinosaurs disappeared 65 million years ago. No one can really (3) show me why for sure, but a (4) few people have made very good guesses. Some think it was (5) because of (6) too much cold weather. Then (7) there are (8) those who say that (9) their food was in short supply. I'd like to (10) read to find (11) out more theories (12) about our great vanishing dinosaurs. Where (13) might information like this be (14) found?

■ Extend Learning

1. Have students share their answer to the story question. Make a list on the chalkboard of the information sources, such as nonfiction library books, textbooks, science magazines, and encyclopedias. Discuss how to locate and use these sources and encourage students to do so. Provide time for sharing new information that is found.
2. Have students find and circle the story phrase *in short supply*. Discuss its meaning. Then have students rewrite the sentence substituting the phrase for words that have the same meaning.
3. Have students circle and write the story words *show* and *found*. Then have students list words that follow these spelling patterns, such as *blow, flow, grow, tow* and *hound, pound, round, sound*. Discuss any unfamiliar words and their meanings.
4. Have students circle and write story word homophones. Choices may include *know, no, for, made, some, to, too, there, their, in, find, might, be, very, great*. Discuss the homophone partners and their meanings. Then ask students to use selected homophones in sentences.

DICTATION REVIEW 37

Materials: pencil, writing paper

Core Words

few	181	always	183	large	185
those	182	show	184		

Review Core Words

of (2), a (4), in (6), is (7), it (10), for (12), are (15), this (22), there (37), can (38), then (53), more (63), see (68), time (69), than (73), who (77), people (79), long (91), very (93), just (97), go (105), too (112), must (126), because (127), place (131), line (161)

Extra Words

held, late, wait, lot

Have students write the sentences as they are dictated.

1. This show is held in a very large place.
2. Then more than just a few can go see it.
3. Those who go too late must wait in line for a long time.
4. This is because there are always a lot of people.

■ Follow-Up Activity

Have students tell in writing what event they think this might be and explain its popularity.

REVIEW 38 | Core Words 186–190

Use after Core Word 190

CLOZE STORY REVIEW 38

Materials: Master 38, pencil, writing paper

Core Words

often	186	asked	188	don't	190
together	187	house	189		

Review Words

they (19), what (32), their (42), said (43), over (82), our (109), think (118), also (119), those (182)

Tell students that this story is about a young lady they may know who does not always use good sense. Read the story as students write the words. Then have students write their answer to the story question.

Amelia Bedelia

Amelia Bedelia is a maid in Peggy Parish's books. She (1) <u>often</u> works for Mr. and Mrs. Rogers in (2) <u>their</u> big (3) <u>house</u>. Once (4) <u>they</u> (5) <u>asked</u> her to bake a sponge cake. As Amelia put the ingredients (6) <u>together</u>, she added a large kitchen sponge. Mrs. Rogers (7) <u>also</u> (8) <u>said</u>, "Now (9) <u>don't</u> forget to dust the furniture and change the towels in (10) <u>our</u> bathroom." So Amelia put dust all (11) <u>over</u> the furniture. (12) <u>What</u> do you (13) <u>think</u> Amelia did with (14) <u>those</u> towels?

■ Extend Learning

1. Have students share their answer to the story question. Discuss Amelia Bedelia's interpretation of "sponge cake" and "dust the furniture." Then read *Amelia Bedelia* by Peggy Parish to see how Amelia interpreted the request to *change the towels*. Students will find that she snipped them with scissors to *change* them. Each of the Amelia Bedelia books in Parish's series helps students humorously understand words with more than one meaning.

2. Have students circle and write the story words *large, sponge, Rogers,* and *change*. Have them listen to the sound the *ge* is making in the words. Then have students find and write more words that have this spelling pattern. Choices may include *charge, huge, age, strange, danger, stage, page*.

3. Have students circle and write the story words *dust* and *bake*. Then write on the chalkboard *Amelia Bedelia was dusting and baking*. Contrast the rule for adding the *ing* suffix to words that end in a consonant and words that end in a consonant and a silent *e*. Then have students find and write more words that illustrate the rule, such as *look, think, help, end, make, use, take, come*.

4. Have students predict the spellings through the word preview procedure of the review story words *put, large, works, now* and the new story words *Mr., Mrs., books, change*. Have students check their predictions against the spelling of the story words.

DICTATION REVIEW 38

Materials: pencil, writing paper

Core Words

often	186	asked	188	don't	190
together	187	house	189		

Review Core Words

the (1), of (2), a (4), to (5), you (8), it (10), at (20), be (21), there (37), their (42), would (59), two (65), time (69), over (82), little (92), after (94), get (101), go (105), come (123), here (134), why (136), different (139), again (141), might (173), next (174), something (178)

Extra Words

school, soon, plan, instead

Have students write the sentences as they are dictated.

1. The two of you often get together at their house after school.
2. You might be asked to go over there again soon.
3. Why don't you plan to come here next time instead?
4. It would be something a little different.

■ Follow-Up Activity

Have students tell in writing where they often get together with their friends to do homework or play. Ask them to give reasons for why this is where they go.

REVIEW 39 | Core Words 191–195

Use after Core Word 195

CLOZE STORY REVIEW 39

Materials: Master 39, pencil, writing paper

Core Words

world	191	want	193	important	195
going	192	school	194		

Review Words

there (37), each (47), right (116), around (120),
another (121), help (137), always (183),
show (184), asked (188)

Tell students that it's time to think about clocks in this story. Read the story as students write the words. Then have students write their answer to the request in the last story sentence.

Tick-Tock Clocks

What time is it? Have you (1) <u>asked</u> that question yet today? People (2) <u>always</u> (3) <u>want</u> to know the time. The (4) <u>world</u> seems to be run by clocks! Clocks (5) <u>help</u> us know when to leave for (6) <u>school</u> (7) <u>each</u> day. They tell us when we're (8) <u>going</u> to lunch and (9) <u>show</u> us the (10) <u>right</u> time to get ready for bed. Clocks are so (11) <u>important</u> that they are all (12) <u>around</u> us. (13) <u>There</u> is an alarm clock, a watch, and a grandfather clock. Write the name of (14) <u>another</u> kind of clock.

■ **Extend Learning**

1. Have students share their answer to the story request. Choices may include a wall clock, digital clock, cuckoo clock, grandmother clock, kitchen timer, stop watch. Ask students to list each place there is a clock at home and at school. Share the noddlehead story *Clocks and More Clocks* by Pat Hutchins in which Mr. Higgins finally solves the problem of keeping all his clocks telling the right time.

2. Have students circle and write the story words *time, run, show, right, watch, kind.* Discuss two different meanings for each of these words. Have students write the words in sentences.

3. Have students circle each of the six occurrences of the word *clock(s)* in the story. Note the sound

that *ck* makes at the end of the word. Then have students find and write more words that end in *ck.* Choices may include *truck, back, black, neck, quick, check, rock, block, stick, pick.*

4. Have students write a new name for this short story and tell why they think the name is a good choice.

DICTATION REVIEW 39

Materials: pencil, writing paper

Core Words

world	191	want	193	important	195
going	192	school	194		

Review Core Words

the (1), to (5), in (6), is (7), you (8), that (9),
for (12), are (15), I (24), but (31), there (37),
your (40), do (45), how (49), then (53), time (69),
first (74), where (98), come(s) (123), always (183),
don't (190)

Extra Words

forget, homework, remember, play

Have students write the sentences as they are dictated. Provide assistance with the comma in the last sentence.

1. Where in the world are you going?
2. I don't want you to forget to do your homework.
3. Always remember how important that is.
4. School comes first, but then there is time for play.

■ **Follow-Up Activity**

Have students describe in writing when someone has said one of these idiomatic phrases to them: *where in the world . . . what in the world . . . why in the world . . . who in the world . . . when in the world.*

REVIEW 40 | Core Words 196–200

Use after Core Word 200

CLOZE STORY REVIEW 40

Materials: Master 40, pencil, writing paper

Core Words

until	196	food	198	children	200
form	197	keep	199		

Review Words

> which (41), their (42), more (63), again (141),
> went (143), great (146), always (183), want (193),
> important (195)

Tell students that they will learn about a successful
athlete in this story. Read the story as students write
the words. Then have students tell about something
they practice (piano, cooking, drawing, soccer,
computer games) to improve their ability to do it.

Perfectly Practiced

(1) <u>Which</u> (2) <u>children</u> will later become
(3) <u>important</u> world athletes? These youngsters
(4) <u>form</u> good sports habits at an early age. They
(5) <u>keep</u> practicing, they eat healthy (6) <u>food</u>, and
in (7) <u>their</u> heart they (8) <u>want</u> to be (9) <u>great</u>.
Nadia Comaneci, a Rumanian gymnast, was one of
these kids. (10) <u>Until</u> Nadia (11) <u>went</u> to the 1976
Olympics, no gymnast had scored a perfect ten! She
did it! Then she did it (12) <u>again</u> seven (13) <u>more</u>
times! She will (14) <u>always</u> be remembered.

■ Extend Learning

1. Have students share their writing and discuss the
   importance of practice for refining skills.
2. Have students find Rumania in southeastern
   Europe on a map. Discuss gymnastics and the
   Olympic Games. Have interested students
   research and write about Comaneci, the Olympics,
   or another favorite world athlete. Recommended
   read-aloud to students: *Bonnie Blair: Golden
   Streak* by Cathy Breitenbucher and *Chris Mullin:
   Sure Shot* by Terri Morgan and Shmuel Thaler,
   both easy biographies about Olympic achievers.
3. Have students circle and write the story words
   one, seven, and *ten.* Have them write more
   number words. Then have them identify the
   homophones among them (one, two, four, eight).
4. Have students circle and write the story word
   children. Then circle the word *child* inside. Repeat
   the activity with *world/or, great/eat, want/ant,
   these/the, always/ways.*
5. Have students circle and write the story words *will,
   good, keep, food, until, always.* Ask students to sort
   them in some way. One method may be words
   with/without double letters. Ask students to explain
   in writing how they chose to sort the words.

DICTATION REVIEW 40

Materials: pencil, writing paper

Core Words

until	196	food	198	children	200
form	197	keep	199		

Review Core Words

> the (1), to (5), in (6), is (7), they (19), at (20),
> one (28), all (33), their (42), them (52), two (65),
> down (84), long (91), very (93), good (106),
> our (109), must (126), place (131), line(s) (161),
> always (183), together (187), ask(ed) (188),
> school (194)

Extra Words

> hall, wait, ready, lunch

Have students write the sentences as they are dictated.
1. Keep the children together in one place.
2. Ask them to form two long lines down the hall.
3. They all must wait until their food is ready.
4. Lunch is always very good at our school.

■ Follow-Up Activity

Have students evaluate whether the request to have the
children wait *in line* is a good one. Why or why not?

REVIEW 41 Core Words 201–205

Use after Core Word 205

CLOZE STORY REVIEW 41

Materials: Master 41, pencil, writing paper

Core Words

feet	201	side	203	boy(s)	205
land	202	without	204		

Review Words

> from (23), their (42), its (76), too (112),
> different (139), home (157), large (185), form (197)

Tell students that this story tells about one of the
National parks in the southwestern part of the United
States. Read the story as students write the words. Then
have students write their answer to the story question.

The Grand Canyon

The Grand Canyon is such a (1) <u>large</u> and beautiful (2) <u>form</u> of (3) <u>land</u>. (4) <u>From</u> one (5) <u>side</u> to the other, it measures up to 18 miles wide. (6) <u>Its</u> steep cliffs plunge over 5,000 (7) <u>feet</u> deep. And (8) <u>without</u> a doubt, it's getting bigger every day! It is the (9) <u>home</u> of over 67 kinds of mammals, 32 reptile species, and 291 (10) <u>different</u> birds. Many (11) <u>boys</u> and girls live with (12) <u>their</u> families in or near the canyon, (13) <u>too</u>. How could such a grand canyon have been created?

■ Extend Learning

1. Have students share their answer to the story question. With research, the students should conclude that Arizona's Grand Canyon began its formation about 6 million years ago when the Colorado River began flowing through the rocky area. Over many years, the erosion caused by the river made the canyon look as it does today. Recommended read-aloud to students: *Grand Canyon* by Patrick Cone that features fine pictures, native plants and animals, and today's conservation efforts.

2. Have students circle and write the story words *Grand Canyon* and *grand canyon*. Ask them to explain in writing why one uses capitals and the other does not.

3. Have students circle and write the story words *land form, canyon, plunge, species, mammals, reptile*. Discuss the meaning of these words. Contrast the story words *form* and *from*.

4. Have students circle and write the story words *its/it's, to/too, and their.* Write the words on the chalkboard and ask the students to identify which homophones are missing from these sets (two, there, they're).

5. Have students circle and write the review story words *other, over, of, one, or.* Review alphabetizing to the second letter. Then have students alphabetize the words.

DICTATION REVIEW 41

Materials: pencil, writing paper

Core Words

feet	201	side	203	boy(s)	205
land	202	without	204		

Review Core Words

the (1), he (11), was (13), on (14), his (18), I (24), by (27), there (37), two (65), him (67), my (80), little (92), where (98), any (113), put (138), asked (188)

Extra Words

lost, standing, shoes, cold

Have students write the sentences as they are dictated.
1. The lost little boy was standing by my side.
2. He was there without any shoes.
3. The land was cold on his two feet.
4. I asked him where he put his shoes.

■ Follow-Up Activity

Have students speculate in writing exactly what they would do if they found a lost child outside their house.

REVIEW 42 Core Words 206–210

Use after Core Word 210

CLOZE STORY REVIEW 42

Materials: Master 42, pencil, writing paper

Core Words

once	206	life	208	took	210
animal	207	enough	209		

Review Words

these (58), find (87), long (91), know (100), back (103), another (121), left (169), thought (179), without (204)

Tell students that this story has a happy ending. Read the story as students write the words. Then have students hypothesize in writing the reaction of the Moore family the moment they saw Tabby Cat.

The Returning Cats

The Moore family had the surprise of their (1) <u>life</u>! Tabby Cat got lost on their vacation to Utah. Sadly, they (2) <u>left</u> for home (3) <u>without</u> her. (4) <u>Once</u> they got (5) <u>back</u> to Idaho, they (6) <u>thought</u> they'd get (7) <u>another</u> cat. Before they did, Tabby showed up! It (8) <u>took</u> the (9) <u>animal</u> three months, but she did return! (10) <u>Enough</u> people have told similar stories for us to (11) <u>know</u> that this is not unusual. But it is a big mystery how (12) <u>these</u> cats (13) <u>find</u> their way (14) <u>long</u> distances home.

Extend Learning

1. Have students share their writing.
2. Have students research stories of returning cats (or dogs) and share the various explanations for a cat's ability to find its way back home. Scientists don't agree. Some think that cats do this by the position of the sun, others believe through a keen sense of smell, and some say it's the cats sense of the earth's magnetic field.
3. Have students circle and write the story words *life, lost, home, told, find*. Then have students change one letter of these words, but not the first letter, to make another word.
4. Have students predict the spellings through the word preview procedure of the review story words *their, home, they, three* and the new story words *family, cat, months, before*. Have students check their predictions against the spelling of the story words.
5. Have students trace on a map a route from Utah to Idaho, naming the route Tabby Cat may have taken on her way home. Have students write what kinds of challenges the cat may have had along the way.
6. Have students find a number word in the story (three). Then have them write the number words one through ten and identify which are homophones (one, two, four, eight).

DICTATION REVIEW 42

Materials: pencil, writing paper

Core Words

once	206	life	208	took	210
animal	207	enough	209		

Review Core Words

the (1), and (3), to (5), is (7), it (10), was (13), we (36), there (37), them (52), these (58), two (65), no (71), water (90), get (101), must (126), help (137), every (151), last (166), something (178), thought (179), important (195), food (198), without (204)

Extra Words

year, deer, eat, things

Have students write the sentences as they are dictated.

1. Once last year we took the deer something to eat.
2. Every animal must get enough food and water.
3. There is no life without these two things.
4. We thought it was important to help them.

■ Follow-Up Activity

Have students tell in writing why they think the deer may have needed more food and water than they were able to provide for themselves (cold and snowy weather, forest fire, drought, etc.). Have students research what kind of food deer eat.

REVIEW 43 Core Words 211–215

Use after Core Word 215

CLOZE STORY REVIEW 43

Materials: Master 43, pencil, writing paper

Core Words

four	211	above	213	began	215
head	212	kind	214		

Review Words

were (34), been (75), use (88), also (119), around (120), air (160), show (184), often (186), took (210)

Tell students that this story includes information that they will be asked to recall. Read the story as students write the words. Then have them answer the questions in item one of the Extend Learning activity.

Is it a Bug or an Insect?

We (1) <u>often</u> (2) <u>use</u> the nickname bugs for all insects. A bug is really one (3) <u>kind</u> of insect. All insects have a (4) <u>head</u>, a thorax, and an abdomen. If the insect is a bug, it (5) <u>also</u> has (6) <u>four</u> wings. Fossils (7) <u>show</u> that insects have (8) <u>been</u> (9) <u>around</u> since life (10) <u>began</u>. Flying insects had the skies (11) <u>above</u> all to themselves long before pterodactyls, birds, or bats (12) <u>took</u> to the (13) <u>air</u>. Some (14) <u>were</u> big. Ancient dragonflies had wings twenty-nine inches wide!

■ Extend Learning

1. Have students practice information recall and thinking skills by asking them to write answers to these questions:
   1. Are all insects bugs? Why or why not?
   2. How do we know that insects have been around since ancient times?
   3. How large were some of the insects of long ago?
   Then review the answers.
2. Have students research bugs and write about a favorite one. One resource is *The Big Bug Book* by Margery Facklam.
3. Have students circle and write the story word *pterodactyl.* See if students can identify it as an extinct flying reptile. *Ptero* is a Greek word part meaning *wing.*
4. Have students circle and write the story words *often, all, head, life, above, before, big, ancient.* Then have students write antonyms for these words.
5. Have students circle and write the story word *nickname.* Discuss the meaning of the word. Then have them write about their own nickname or that of a friend or relative.

DICTATION REVIEW 43

Materials: pencil, writing paper

Core Words

four	211	above	213	began	215
head	212	kind	214		

Review Core Words

the (1), of (2), to (5), for (12), they (19), at (20), be (21), had (29), not (30), what (32), there (37), their (42), about (48), them (52), been (75), way (86), find (87), day (114), work(ers) (124), help(ed) (137), home (157), might (173), thought (179), house (189), food (198), enough (209)

Extra Words

full, moon, eat, during

Have students write the sentences as they are dictated
1. The four workers began to head for home.
2. The full moon above helped them find their way.
3. They thought about what kind of food might be at their house.
4. There had not been enough to eat during the day.

■ Follow-Up Activity

Have students describe in writing what food they might be thinking about if they were one of the weary, hungry workers heading for home.

REVIEW 44 Core Words 216–220

Use after Core Word 220

CLOZE STORY REVIEW 44

Materials: Master 44, pencil, writing paper

Core Words

almost	216	page	218	earth	220
live	217	got	219		

Review Words

there (37), first (74), through (102), another (121), off (142), always (183), without (204), life (208), head (212)

Tell students that this story is about something we use many times a day. Read the story as students write the words. Then have students continue this story on another sheet of paper.

How Important is Paper?

Could you (1) <u>live</u> (2) <u>without</u> paper? (3) <u>Life</u> would surely change if you took all the paper (4) <u>off</u> this (5) <u>earth</u>. Let's follow you (6) <u>through</u> a day. (7) <u>First</u>, you (8) <u>head</u> for the bathroom. (9) <u>There</u> is no toilet paper! Don't try to blow your nose either. No tissue. You (10) <u>almost</u> (11) <u>always</u> have breakfast cereal, but it's not in a box. Find a new container for your sack lunch, too. Where's the sports (12) <u>page</u>? (13) <u>Got</u> the picture? Continue this, on (14) <u>another</u> sheet of . . . *paper.*

■ Extend Learning

1. Have students share their story continuations. Then have students work in pairs to list paper products. Then share their lists.

2. Have students circle and write the story word *too*. Then write its homophones *to* and *two*. Next, ask students to use these three homophones in written sentences. Repeat the activity with the story words *there, through, it's*.

3. Have students circle and write the story words *almost* and *always*. Then ask them to write the review word *also*. Add to the lesson the words *already, although, altogether*. Have students underline *al* in each word. Compare the words with *all right*.

4. Have students circle and write the story word compounds (without, bathroom, breakfast, another). Then have them find and write more compound words.

5. Have students circle and write the story word contractions (let's, don't, it's, where's). Have students write the words that comprise each contraction.

DICTATION REVIEW 44

Materials: pencil, writing paper

Core Words

almost	216	page	218	earth	220
live	217	got	219		

Review Core Words

the (1), of (2), a (4), to (5), in (6), it (10), was (13), on (14), they (19), this (22), I (24), were (34), each (47), about (48), how (49), out (51), other (60), see (68), could (70), who (77), people (79), know (100), get (101), our (109), me (110), help(ed) (137), read (165), side (203)

Extra Words

story, lot, book, family

Have students write the sentences as they are dictated.

1. I could almost see the people who were in the story.
2. Each page I read helped me get to know how they live.
3. I got a lot out of this book.
4. It was about a family on the other side of our earth.

■ Follow-Up Activity

Have students find places on a map that may have been the setting for this story. Have them identify a story that told about people who lived a life different from their own. Then have them tell in writing how these people's lives were different from their own . . . as well as ways in which they were the same.

REVIEW 45 Core Words 221–225

Use after Core Word 225

CLOZE STORY REVIEW 45

Materials: Master 45, pencil, writing paper

Core Words

need	221	hand	223	year	225
far	222	high	224		

Review Words

they (19), could (70), than (73), again (141), thought (179), don't (190), school (194), once (206), enough (209)

Tell students that this story has a money-making idea for them. Read the story as students write the words. Then have students write about another way children can earn money and help others at the same time.

You're in Business

Have you ever (1) <u>thought</u> of starting an errand service after (2) <u>school</u>? Busy people (3) <u>need</u> help. You (4) <u>could</u> give them a (5) <u>hand</u> running errands that (6) <u>don't</u> take you (7) <u>far</u> from home. Charge for your service, but not too (8) <u>high</u> a price. You want them to call you (9) <u>again</u>. Your business will grow (10) <u>once</u> folks know (11) <u>they</u> can count on you. Before the school (12) <u>year</u> is over, you'll have more (13) <u>than</u> (14) <u>enough</u> business and a cookie jar full of cash!

■ Extend Learning

1. Have students share their writing.
2. Have students brainstorm for information necessary for a flyer announcing a fictitious errand service. This may include kinds of errands (groceries, drug store, post office, library),

charges, days and times available for work, name, phone, address. Then have students create the flyer and share it with the class. Have students evaluate each flyer to see if it includes all the information an interested person may need.

3. Have students circle and write the story words that have more than one meaning. Choices may include *hand, running, too, home, charge, service, can, count, over.*

4. Have students circle and write the story word contractions (you're, don't, you'll). Then have them write the words that comprise each contraction.

5. Have students circle and write the story word *running* and write its base word *run.* Note how the final consonant doubles before the addition of the suffix. Have students find and write more words that follow this spelling pattern. Choices may include *cut, get, let, put, set, stop.*

6. Have students circle and write the two occurrences of the review story word *school,* one of the most frequently misspelled words. Have students write how their school was named. Then have them choose another name for their school and tell why the name is a good one.

DICTATION REVIEW 45

Materials: pencil, writing paper

Core Words

need	221	hand	223	year 225
far	222	high	224	

Review Core Words

a (4), to (5), in (6), you (8), that (9), are (15), be (21), or (26), when (35), your (40), do (45), will (46), how (49), two (65), over (82), think (118), place (131), put (138), old (144), big (158), left (169), might (173), head (212), above (213)

Extra Words

please, arm, grow, tall

Have students write the sentences as they are dictated.

1. Please place your left hand high over your head.
2. You need to put your arm far above you.
3. Will you grow that big in a year or two?
4. How old do you think you might be when you are that tall?

■ Follow-Up Activity

Have students tell in writing how tall they think they will be when they are fully grown. Then have students tell why they think this height will, or will not, be a good height.

REVIEW 46 | Core Words 226–230

Use after Core Word 230

CLOZE STORY REVIEW 46

Materials: Master 46, pencil, writing paper

Core Words

mother	226	country	228	let	230
light	227	father	229		

Review Words

there (37), their (42), know (100), write (108), too (112), while (172) something (178), food (198), once (206)

Tell students that this familiar story needs a new ending. Read the story as students write the words. Then have students write their new story ending.

Old Tale, New Ending

"(1) Once upon a time, (2) there was a bear family living happily in a (3) country cottage. One morning when the (4) mother, the (5) father, and the baby bear sat down to eat (6) their porridge, it was (7) too hot. So they turned off the (8) light and took a walk in the woods to (9) let the (10) food cool." You (11) know what happened in this story (12) while the bears were away. However, this time (13) something else happened. (14) Write what took place in a new version of the tale.

■ Extend Learning

1. Have students share their new version of the story ending. Compile the versions into a class book.

2. Have students circle and write the story word homophones. Choices may include *there, bear, in, one, morning, to, too, their, so, know, write, new, tale.* Discuss and write the homophone partners. Then have students use selected homophones in sentences.

3. Have students circle and write the story word *cottage.* Then have them find and write words that name a place in which to live. These may include the review words *home* and *house,* as well as *pad, apartment, flat, castle, palace, residence, estate, condo, condominium, mansion, abode, boathouse, igloo, duplex, triplex, cabin, tent, bungalow.* Discuss the meanings of unfamiliar words.

4. Have students circle and write the story words *down, hot, off, cool, new.* Then have them write the antonyms of these words.

DICTATION REVIEW 46

Materials: pencil, writing paper

Core Words

mother	226	country	228	let	230
light	227	father	229		

Review Core Words

the (1), and (3), to (5), for (12), on (14), they (19), at (20), from (23), I (24), not (30), many (55), my (80), did (83), after (94), get (101), back (103), go (105), our (109), me (110), went (143), home (157), left (169), show (184), together (187), school (194), until (196), children (200)

Extra Words

outside, dark, music, fair

Have students write the sentences as they are dictated.
1. My mother and father left the outside light on for me.
2. I did not get back home until after dark.
3. They let me go to the country music show at the fair.
4. Many children from our school went together.

■ Follow-Up Activity

Have students tell in writing about a music show they would like to attend. Then have them create a newspaper announcement advertising the upcoming concert.

REVIEW 47 Core Words 231–235

Use after Core Word 235

CLOZE STORY REVIEW 47

Materials: Master 47, pencil, writing paper

Core Words

night	231	being	233	second	235
picture	232	study	234		

Review Words

there (37), new (107), around (120), off (142), world (191), without (204), almost (216), earth (220), light (227)

Tell students that this story sets the scene for some big problems. Read the story as students write the words. Then have students write their descriptions.

The Day With No Electricity

(1) Study this (2) picture in your head. It is (3) night at your house. For the time (4) being, (5) almost everyone for miles (6) around is asleep. But before the (7) light of a (8) new day begins, all the electricity on (9) earth goes (10) off! What happens? First, if you have an electric alarm clock, you sleep on. But the (11) second you do awake, (12) there is a (13) world of problems ahead for you and others. Describe the difficulties that may arise on this "day (14) without electricity."

■ Extend Learning

1. Have students share their descriptions of the "day without electricity."
2. Have students circle and write the story words *with no* (in title) and *without.* Discuss their synonymous meaning. Then ask students to replace these story words and phrases with ones that mean nearly the same thing: *study, picture, house, for the time being, almost, asleep, awake, world of problems, arise.* Next, ask students to read their new story to a partner inserting the replacement words or phrases.
3. Have students circle and write the story words *around, asleep, awake, ahead, arise.* Then have them find and write more *a ___* words.

4. Have students circle and write the story words that rhyme. Choices may include *night/light, new/you/do, for/your, that/at, may/day.* Note that rhyming words do not always have the same spelling patterns.

DICTATION REVIEW 47

Materials: pencil, writing paper

Core Words

night	231	being	233	second	235
picture	232	study	234		

Review Core Words

the (1), of (2), and (3), a (4), to (5), in (6), is (7), it (10), at (20), be (21), this (22), I (24), or (26), when (35), there (37), can (38), do (45), then (53), two (65), like (66), time (69), my (80), only (85), go (105), place (131), world (191), want (193), form (197), head (212), almost (216)

Extra Words

anywhere, really, being, sleep

Have students write the sentences as they are dictated.
1. I can be anywhere in the world in only a second or two.
2. I form a picture in my head of the place I want to be.
3. Then I study it and it is almost like really being there.
4. I do this at night when it is time to go to sleep.

■ Follow-Up Activity

Ask students to form a picture in their head of a place they'd like to spend the day tomorrow. Then state reasons why this place is their first choice.

REVIEW 48 — Core Words 236–240

Use after Core Word 240

CLOZE STORY REVIEW 48

Materials: Master 48, pencil, writing paper

Core Words

soon	236	since	238	ever	240
story	237	white	239		

Review Words

they (19), been (75), people (79), write (108), together (187), house (189), important (195), above (213), began (215), year (225)

Tell students that this story tells about the history of Washington, DC and some of its important buildings. Read the story, excluding the title, as students write the words. Then have students write why they think this is, or is not, a good name for the President's home.

The (1) White (2) House

In the (3) year 1814, the British invaded America's capital city. (4) They burned much of the President's mansion and other (5) important government buildings. The American (6) people quickly (7) began to work (8) together making plans to rebuild. (9) Soon their city was like new. The President's mansion sparkled with fresh paint. (10) Ever (11) since then, this great mansion has (12) been known by a special name. (13) Write this distinctive name (14) above for the (15) story title.

■ Extend Learning

1. Have students share their story title and their written opinion of the name for the President's home.
2. Have students circle and write the story word *distinctive.* Ask students for synonyms for this word. Choices may include *unusual, unique, special, significant.*
3. Have students circle and write the story word *their,* the most frequently misspelled (or misused) word in English. Have students explain in writing how to differentiate between *their* and *there.*
4. Have students circle and write the story word *rebuild.* Have them underline the base word *build.* Explain the meaning and use of the prefix *re.* Discuss the addition of the *re* prefix to the review words *make, use, new, place, tell, name, read, live, study.* Then have students find and write more words that use the *re* prefix.
5. Have students predict the spellings through the word preview procedure of the review story words *much, other, great, new* and the new story words *city, paint, title, making.* Have students check their predictions against the spelling of the story words.

DICTATION REVIEW 48

Materials: pencil, writing paper

Core Words

soon	236	since	238	ever	240
story	237	white	239		

Review Core Words

the (1), a (4), to (5), it (10), for (12), are (15), be (21), I (24), there (37), do (45), will (46), about (48), out (51), then (53), many (55), would (59), like (66), water (90), our (109), read (165), want(ed) (193), school (194)

Extra Words

rafting, try, summer, things

Have students write the sentences as they are dictated.
1. I read a story about white water rafting.
2. Ever since then I wanted to try it.
3. Soon our school will be out for the summer.
4. Then there are many things I would like to do.

■ Follow-Up Activity

Have students write about something they have not done, but would like to do. Then tell why they want to do it.

REVIEW 49   Core Words 241–245

Use after Core Word 245

CLOZE STORY REVIEW 49

Materials: Master 49, pencil, writing paper

Core Words

paper	241	near	243	better	245
hard	242	sentence	244		

Review Words

what (32), were (34), your (40), now (78), through (102), think (118), because (127), place (131), something (178)

Tell students that this story asks them to think and write. Read the story as students write the words. Then have students write directions for doing something that can be demonstrated in class.

How To Do It

Get (1) <u>paper</u> and pencil. (2) <u>Place</u> a dictionary (3) <u>near</u> you. (4) <u>Now</u> write the directions for how to do (5) <u>something</u>. You might find this (6) <u>hard</u> (7) <u>because</u> every step must be included. Each (8) <u>sentence</u> should say exactly (9) <u>what</u> you mean. When you are (10) <u>through</u>, reread the directions and rewrite the parts you (11) <u>think</u> you can make (12) <u>better</u>. Then ask a friend to follow (13) <u>your</u> directions. This will tell you how well the directions you wrote (14) <u>were</u> written.

■ Extend Learning

1. Have students report how well their directions were written. If steps were missing, have students rewrite the directions to clearly state each step. Compile the students' directions into a class book.

2. Have students circle and write the story word *write* and each of its other word forms used in the story (rewrite, wrote, written). Then have students write more forms of *write*. Choices may include *writing, writes, writer, writers, prewriting*.

3. Have students circle and write the story word *through*. Then have them write its homophone (threw). Have students find and write more words that contain the spelling *ough*, such as *bought, enough, brought, though, rough*.

4. Have students circle and write the story words *reread* and *rewrite*. Review the *re* prefix (Extend Learning, Review 48).

5. Have students recall and write the word *directions*. Then check the spelling with the story word. Ask students to circle its four occurrences.

DICTATION REVIEW 49

Materials: pencil, writing paper

Core Words

paper	241	near	243	better	245
hard	242	sentence	244		

Review Core Words

and (3), a (4), to (5), is (7), you (8), for (12), or (26), what (32), can (38), do (45), about (48), them (52), these (58), other(s) (60), two (65), than (73), get (101), write (108), think (118), put (138), something (178)

Extra Words

    pencil, somewhere, sometimes, things

Have students write the sentences as they are dictated.

1. Get paper and pencil and put them somewhere near you.
2. Think about something you can do better than others.
3. What is sometimes hard for you to do?
4. Write a sentence or two about these things.

■ Follow-Up Activity

Have students share their writing about what they do well and what they find hard to do. Then reinforce that practice helps people improve their skills.

REVIEW 50   Core Words 246–250

Use after Core Word 250

CLOZE STORY REVIEW 50

Materials: Master 50, pencil, writing paper

Core Words

best	246	during	248	however	250
across	247	today	249		

Review Words

    said (43), then (53), could (70), very (93),
why (136), air (160), never (167),
something (178), world (191)

Tell students that this story tells about William Ernest's invention. Read the story as students write the words. Then have students write their answer to the story question.

Water Wings for Horses

    The "spirit of invention" has changed the (1) world! (2) However, some inventions (3) never became popular. (4) During the era of horse travel, William Ernest invented (5) something that he (6) said was the (7) best way to cross deep rivers. It was two (8) very big rubber bags that (9) could be filled with (10) air to attach to a horse's stomach. (11) Then horse and rider would float (12) across the river. (13) Why do you think this invention is not one we remember (14) today?

■ Extend Learning

1. Have students share their answer to the story question.
2. Discuss with students the meaning of *spirit of invention.* Ask students if they know the names of any inventors and their inventions. Interested students can research and report to the class information about inventors and their inventions.
3. Have students circle and write the story words *cross* and *across.* Then have students write a sentence using each word. Extend the lesson to *long/along, live/alive, round/around, head/ahead, way/away.*
4. Have students circle and write the story word homophones. Choices may include *horse, some, way, to, two, very, be, would, do, you, not, one.* Have students write the homophone partners of these words.
5. Have students predict the spellings through the word preview procedure of the review story words *some, two, would, think* and the new story words *horse, rivers, changed.* Have students check their predictions against the spelling of the story words.

DICTATION REVIEW 50

Materials: pencil, writing paper

Core Words

best	246	during	248	however	250
across	247	today	249		

Review Core Words

    the (1), to (5), from (23), all (33), we (36),
will (46), then (53), her (64), make(s) (72),
my (80), go (105), our (109), help (137),
together (187), house (189), school (194),
food (198), live(s) (217), mother (226)

Extra Words

    friend, street, lunch, eat

Have students write the sentences as they are dictated. Provide assistance with the comma in the third sentence.

1. My best friend lives across the street from our school.
2. Today we will go to her house during lunch.
3. Her mother makes the food, however we help.
4. Then we all eat together.

■ **Follow-Up Activity**

Have students draw and describe in writing their favorite lunch.

REVIEW 51 | Core Words 251-255

Use after Core Word 255

CLOZE STORY REVIEW 51

Materials: Master 51, pencil, writing paper

Core Words

sure	251	it's	253	told	255
knew	252	try	254		

Review Words

there (37), then (53), its (76), still (153), often (186), once (206), began (215), today (249), however (250)

Tell students that this story will have them singing. Read the story as students write the words. Then have students recall and write the words to the familiar song, "Happy Birthday."

Sing a Song

(1) <u>There</u> is a song you (2) <u>knew</u> when you were little that you (3) <u>still</u> sing (4) <u>today</u>. It is (5) <u>sure</u> to be sung to you (6) <u>once</u> a year. We are (7) <u>told</u> that (8) <u>it's</u> the most (9) <u>often</u> sung song! Mildred Hill, a Kentucky teacher, wrote the melody and her sister Patty Hill, a principal, wrote (10) <u>its</u> words. (11) <u>However</u>, long ago the words (12) <u>began</u>, "Good morning to all, Good morning to all." (13) <u>Try</u> to sing this song with these words. (14) <u>Then</u> write it the way all of us know it best.

■ **Extend Learning**

1. Write the words to "Happy Birthday" on the chalkboard so that students may check their work against it. Discuss the meaning of *melody*. Follow up with students writing the words to one of their favorite songs.

2. Have students circle and write the story words *it's* and *its*. Have them explain in writing how these words are used differently.

3. Have students circle and write the story words *still, long,* and *way*. Then have students write each word in two sentences, each sentence using a different meaning for the word. Have students share their sentences.

4. Have students find and circle the story words *when, were, wrote, words, with, way*. Then have students write the words in alphabetical order.

5. Have students circle and write the story words *knew/know, sung/sing*. Then have them write these past tense story words with their present tense: *told, wrote, began*.

DICTATION REVIEW 51

Materials: pencil, writing paper

Core Words

sure	251	it's	253	told	255
knew	252	try	254		

Review Core Words

the (1), and (3), to (5), on (14), they (19), be (21), by (27), were (34), an (39), their (42), do (45), will (46), very (93), show (184), want(ed) (193), school (194), important (195), children (200), mother(s) (226), father(s) (229), night (231), soon (236), hard (242), best (246)

Extra Words

play, music, begin, stage, everyone

Have students write the sentences as they are dictated.

1. The school play and music show will soon begin.
2. It's sure to be an important night on the stage.
3. The children were told by everyone to try very hard.
4. Their mothers and fathers knew they wanted to do their best.

■ **Follow-Up Activity**

Based on what the sentences say, have students write how they think the children in the school play and music show are feeling. Have students write about a time they felt the same way.

REVIEW 52 — Core Words 256–260

CLOZE STORY REVIEW 52

Materials: Master 52, pencil, writing paper

Core Words

young	256	thing	258	hear	260
sun	257	whole	259		

Review Words

there (37), said (43), little (92), don't (190), important (195), picture (232), since (238), across (247), knew (252)

Tell students that this story tells about a boy who had a wish. Read the story as students write the words. Then have students write their answer to the story question.

To Fly Like a Hawk

(1) <u>There</u> was only one (2) <u>thing</u> that Rudy wanted in the (3) <u>whole</u> world. Ever (4) <u>since</u> he was a very (5) <u>young</u> child, he (6) <u>knew</u> he wanted to fly. He did not (7) <u>picture</u> himself flying like a (8) <u>little</u> sparrow, but soaring (9) <u>across</u> the sky like a hawk! Up to the (10) <u>sun</u> he would glide! He would be able to (11) <u>hear</u> the wind! However, everyone (12) <u>said</u>, "People (13) <u>don't</u> fly." Yet, Rudy had a wish. Have you a wish? Write about your wish and tell why it's (14) <u>important</u> to you.

■ Extend Learning

1. Have students share their answer to the story question. Then read the Caldecott-winning book *Hawk, I'm Your Brother* by Byrd Baylor and illustrated by Peter Parnall. The story tells about Rudy Soto's wish to fly. Have students predict in writing prior to the reading how Rudy satisfied his wish.
2. Have students circle the story words *people, wanted, would, about.* These are among the most frequently misspelled words. Have students work in pairs to test each other on the spelling of these words, or any other story words.
3. Have students circle and write the story word homophones. Choices may include *there, one, in, whole, very, knew, to, not, sun, would, be, hear,* *you, write, it's.* Discuss and write the homophone partners of these words.
4. Have students circle and write story words for which they can write an antonym, such as *young* (old), *little* (big), *up* (down), *don't* (do).

DICTATION REVIEW 52

Materials: pencil, writing paper

Core Words

young	256	thing(s)	258	hear	260
sun	257	whole	259		

Review Core Words

the (1), of (2), a (4), be (21), or (26), when (35), we (36), about (48), how (49), would (59), could (70), know (100), any (113), day (114), another (121), here (134), different (139), read (165), without (204), began (215), live (217)

Extra Words

lot, hot, summer, plant, sunlight

Have students write the sentences as they are dictated. Provide assistance with the comma in the first sentence.

1. Without the sun, a whole lot of things would be different here.
2. Would we hear or read about a hot summer?
3. Could a young plant live without any sunlight?
4. How would we know when another day began?

■ Follow-Up Activity

After discussing the questions posed, have students write a description of our earth without a sun. How would things be different? Would there be life as we know it?

REVIEW 53 — Core Words 261–265

CLOZE STORY REVIEW 53

Materials: Master 53, pencil, writing paper

Core Words

example	261	several	263	answer	265
heard	262	change	264		

Review Words

their (42), said (43), some (56), would (59), could (70), use (88), thought (179), during (248), today (249)

Tell students that this story tells about an ancient tradition that helped some people make decisions. Read the story as students write the words. Then ask students to write when a "flip of the coin" might be a good way to make a decision and when it would be a poor way to make a decision.

Flip a Coin

(1) <u>During</u> ancient times, people (2) <u>thought</u> it was best to let the gods make (3) <u>their</u> big decisions for them. The people (4) <u>would</u> ask the gods a question and hope the gods (5) <u>heard</u> it. Then they waited for an (6) <u>answer</u> that (7) <u>could</u> come to them in one of (8) <u>several</u> ways. For (9) <u>example</u>, people might (10) <u>use</u> pocket (11) <u>change</u> to flip a coin. If it landed heads, that meant the gods (12) <u>said</u> "yes." Tails meant "no." We still flip a coin to decide (13) <u>some</u> things (14) <u>today</u>.

■ Extend Learning

1. Have students share their writing. Note that the "flip of the coin" on the football field often decides which team is first to have the ball at the opening of a game. Then have students work in pairs to make a list of other ways people sometimes decide who goes first, such as "pick a number," "choose the longest straw," or alphabetical order.

2. Have students circle and write these story words or phrases: *during ancient times, for example, several, flip, might.* Then have students write a word or phrase for each that could be used in its place without changing the meaning.

3. Have students circle the story word *they* each time it occurs in the story (4). Then write the word.

4. The opposite of *heads* on a coin is called *tails.* Have students find story words for which they can write opposites, or antonyms.

5. Have students predict the spellings through the word preview procedure of the review story words *people, head(s), they, might* and the new story words *question, hope, tails, coin.* Have students check their predictions against the spelling of the story words.

DICTATION REVIEW 53

Materials: pencil, writing paper

Core Words

example(s) 261   several 263   answer 265

heard   262   change 264

Review Core Words

the (1), and (3), to (5), in (6), was (13), I (24), had (29), how (49), she (54), her (64), people (79), my (80), write (108), think (118), great (146), might (173), asked (188), world (191), head (212), began (215), soon (236), hard (242), young (256)

Extra Words

test, question, ready, gave

Have students write the sentences as they are dictated.
1. She asked how young people might change the world.
2. I heard the test question and began to think hard.
3. Soon I had the answer in my head and was ready to write.
4. I gave her several great examples.

■ Follow-Up Activity

Have students write several good examples of how young people can make a positive impact on the world, even in a small way. Make a class book of the ideas.

REVIEW 54 — Core Words 266–270

Use after Core Word 270

CLOZE STORY REVIEW 54

Materials: Master 54, pencil, writing paper

Core Words

room   266   against 268   turned 270

sea   267   top   269

Review Words

what (32), were (34), some (56), called (96), much (104), because (127), small (150), name (155), father (229)

Tell students that this story tells about a young girl they may know who had a big imagination. Read the story as students write the words. Then have students write their answer to the story question.

■ Extend Learning

1. Have students share their tall tales. Then read the Caldecott-winning book *Sam, Bangs and Moonshine*, written and illustrated by Evaline Ness. This is the story of Samantha and the troubles her tales cause others. Following the reading, have students explain in writing whether they think the book's title is, or is not, a good one.

2. Have students circle and write the story words *small, mind, name, might*. For each word, have students list rhyming words that follow the same spelling pattern.

3. Have students circle the frequently misspelled story words *people, because, some, against, always, were, what*. Ask students to alphabetize the words.

4. Have students circle and write the story words *lived, called, watching, turned, telling*. Then have students work in pairs to list the other word forms for these words.

DICTATION REVIEW 54

Materials: pencil, writing paper

Core Words

room	266	against	268	turned	270
sea	267	top	269		

Review Core Words

the (1), of (2), a (4), to (5), in (6), it (10), at (20), I (24), were (34), said (43), about (48), then (53), my (80), made (81), over (82), write (108), name (155), below (176), page (218), picture (232), white (239), paper (241), told (255)

Extra Words

drawing, waves, blue, sky

Have students write the sentences as they are dictated. Provide assistance with the comma in the second sentence.

1. At the top of my paper I made a picture of the sea.
2. In the room below the drawing, I told about it.
3. I said the waves were white against the blue sky.
4. Then I turned the page over to write my name.

■ Follow-Up Activity

Have students create a fictitious journal entry about a day at the seashore.

REVIEW 55 — Core Words 271–275

Use after Core Word 275

CLOZE STORY REVIEW 55

Materials: Master 55, pencil, writing paper

Core Words

learn	271	city	273	toward	275
point	272	play	274		

Review Words

were (34), which (41), about (48), little (92), children (200), four (211), country (228), ever (240), young (256)

Tell students that this story tells of a rhyme that is a favorite of young children, as well as a famous inventor. Read the story as students write the words. Then have students recall and write this familiar poem.

■ Extend Learning

1. Write the words to "Mary Had a Little Lamb" on the chalkboard so that students may check their work against the words. Sarah Hale's *Mary Had a Little Lamb* provides a new presentation of this rhyme in an art technique called fabric relief, using embroidery and a variety of textured fabrics and natural surfaces that post-preschool students can appreciate.

2. Have students research when Thomas Edison said the first lines of the rhyme into his invention, the phonograph. Conclude that this took place on November 20, 1877. Then have students write or tell about how the phonograph has evolved into the modern equipment we use today for the same purpose. Some students may wish to research other Thomas Edison inventions, such as the electric light (1879).

3. Have students circle the two occurrences of *lamb* in the story. Then have students find and write more words that end in a silent *b*, such as *comb, dumb, climb, bomb, tomb, limb*.

4. Have students circle and write the story words that have more than one meaning. Choices may include *play, lines, point, short, real*. Discuss the meanings of the words.

5. Have students circle and write the story word *its*. Then have them explain in writing why the use of *its* is correct and *it's* would be incorrect.

DICTATION REVIEW 55

Materials: pencil, writing paper

Core Words

learn	271	city	273	toward	275
point	272	play	274		

Review Core Words

the (1), of (2), and (3), a (4), in (6), is (7), you (8), on (14), with (17), have (25), what (32), when (35), can (38), your (40), which (41), out (51), first (74), look (117), part (129), name (155), next (174), something (178), live (217), far (222), country (228), pictures(d) (232), top (269)

Extra Words

fun, map, please, north

Have students write the sentences as they are dictated. Provide assistance with the commas.

1. You can learn something and have fun when you play with a map.
2. First, point out the city in which you live on your map.
3. Next, please look toward the top part of the map.
4. What is the name of the country pictured in the far north?

■ Follow-Up Activity

Have students use a map to write map questions, such as the one posed in the fourth sentence. Then have students exchange questions and write the answers.

REVIEW 56 · Core Words 276–280

Use after Core Word 280

CLOZE STORY REVIEW 56

Materials: Master 56, pencil, writing paper

Core Words

five	276	usually	278	seen	280
himself	277	money	279		

Review Words

number (145), always (183), kind (214), paper (241), however (250), sure (251), it's (253), try (254), told (255), example (261), answer (265)

Tell students this story is a math puzzle that will surely make them think. Read the story as students write the words. Then have students write their answer to the story question, including *how* they arrived at their answer.

Mystery Coins

Jason was proud of (1) himself. Of course, part of his success may be (2) seen as good luck. (3) However, luck (4) usually runs out after awhile and Jason was (5) always right on his first (6) try. This is the (7) kind of thing Jason could do. If you secretly wrote on a piece of (8) paper an amount of (9) money and the (10) number of coins it took to total that amount, Jason could tell you the coins. For (11) example, you might say, "The amount I have is sixty cents. (12) It's made up of (13) five coins." Jason was (14) sure to have the correct (15) answer. What would Jason have (16) told you?

■ Extend Learning

1. Have students share their answer to the story question and their explanation for how they arrived at their answer (one quarter, three dimes, one nickel). Then have students play Mystery Coins (there is always only one answer). Ask students to write their own secret amount of money on a piece of paper with the number of coins it took to total that amount. Then play this game in small groups giving students an opportunity to provide Jason's right answer.

2. Have students circle and write the story word *himself*. Then have students write *myself*. Have students write a story, "A Time When I was Proud of Myself."

3. Have students circle and write the story word homophones. Choices may include *be, seen, right, do, you, wrote, piece, to, might, cents, it's, made, would, told*. Then have students write the homophone partners for these words.

4. Have students circle and write the story word *told*. Then change the *t* and make new words, such as *bold, hold, fold*. Repeat the activity with the story words *made* (blade, fade, shade), *right* (bright, sight light), and *kind* (find, blind, mind).

DICTATION REVIEW 56

Materials: pencil, writing paper

Core Words

five	276	usually	278	seen	280
himself	277	money	279		

Review Core Words

the (1), of (2), to (5), he (11), his (18), had (29), she (54), him (67), where (98), good (106), look (117), around (120), such (133), help (137), put (138), asked (188), important (195), boy (205), took (210), began (215), mother (226)

Extra Words

birthday, care, anything, dollars

Have students write the sentences as they are dictated.

1. The boy asked himself where he put his birthday money.
2. He usually took such good care of anything important.
3. Had his mother seen his five dollars?
4. She began to help him look around.

■ Follow-Up Activity

Have students write advice for the boy featured in the sentences. Do the students have a system for remembering where they put something important? What is their advice to keep important things from getting lost?

REVIEW 57 | Core Words 281–285

Use after Core Word 285

CLOZE STORY REVIEW 57

Materials: Master 57, pencil, writing paper

Core Words

didn't	281	morning	283	body	285
car	282	I'm	284		

Review Words

said (43), right (116), because (127), does (128), thought (179), soon (236), best (246), try (254), several (263), himself (277), usually (278)

Tell students that this story helps us see the difference between things we *need* and things we *want*. Read the story as students write the words. Then have students write their answer to the story question.

How Do Advertisements Persuade?

   "(1) I'm not going to buy a new automobile (2) because I don't need one." That's what the man (3) said before he saw the (4) car advertised in the (5) morning newspaper. He was (6) right when he said he (7) didn't *need* one, but the ad made him *want* one. The ad showed the (8) body of the auto and gave (9) several reasons to buy it. (10) Soon the man (11) thought this auto was the (12) best thing for (13) himself and his family. The ad worked! An ad (14) usually attempts to persuade you to buy something. Find an ad. How (15) does it (16) try to persuade you to buy?

■ Extend Learning

1. Have students share their ad and their explanation for how the ad persuades the reader to buy something. Then have students create a persuasive ad for a product that could be used by their classmates.

Write the story words *car, auto,* and *automobile* on the chalkboard. Have students find and circle them in the story. Discuss the synonyms. Then have students circle and write the story words *buy, said, right, several, attempts.* Next, ask students to substitute a synonym for each of these words in the story that will not change the meaning. Have students circle and write the story compounds *newspaper* and *something.* Then have students find and write more compound words in a timed write (about three minutes). Award one point for each correctly spelled compound word. Have students circle and write the story word contractions (I'm, don't, that's, didn't). Then have them write the words that comprise these contractions.

DICTATION REVIEW 57

Materials: pencil, writing paper

Core Words

didn't	281	morning	283	body	285
car	282	I'm	284		

Review Core Words

the (1), of (2), to (5), in (6), that (9), they (19), this (22), have (25), all (33), we (36), would (59), could (70), my (80), over (82), too (112), because (127), say (149), last (166), us (168), school (194), far (222), mother (226), night (231), today (249), it's (253), sun (257), whole (259)

Extra Words

cold, drive, walk, weather

Have students write the sentences as they are dictated.

1. I'm cold all over my whole body this morning.
2. Didn't they say last night that we would have sun today?
3. Could mother drive us to school in the car?
4. It's too far to walk because of the weather.

Follow-Up Activity

Have students think of something they would like someone to do for them (such as have someone drive them to school). Then have students explain how they would go about persuading the person to do it.

CLOZE STORY REVIEW 58

Materials: Master 58, pencil, writing paper

Core Words

upon	286	later	288	move	290
family	287	turn	289		

Review Words

its (76), water (90), most (99), another (121), work (124), often (186), once (206), animal(s) (207), sure (251), it's (253), several (263)

Tell students that this story may give them a good idea for a new family pet. Read the story as students write the words. Then have students list animals that make good family pets.

Catch Yourself a Pet

(1) <u>Several</u> kinds of (2) <u>animals</u> make good (3) <u>family</u> pets. A frog is one. Try to catch a frog. Frogs are (4) <u>often</u> found (5) <u>upon</u> a rock by a pond. (6) <u>It's</u> hard to sneak up on a frog and catch it in your hands. (7) <u>Most</u> frogs (8) <u>move</u> quickly. A net at the end of a long pole may (9) <u>work</u> better. (10) <u>Once</u> captured, be gentle. (11) <u>Turn</u> your frog loose inside a big box. This will be (12) <u>its</u> home. Be (13) <u>sure</u> there's (14) <u>water</u> in a tray at the bottom. Feed your new pet flies, worms, and spiders. (15) <u>Later</u>, put your frog back where you caught it. Then go catch (16) <u>another</u> one.

■ Extend Learning

1. Have students share their lists of animals that make good family pets. Vote on the pet the class thinks is the best pet for children their age. Share the humorous poems and stories in *Preposterous Pets* by Laura Cecil. Then have students write about a preposterous pet.

2. Have students circle and write the story words *caught* and *captured.* Discuss how these words mean nearly the same thing. Then have students circle and write the story words *several, near,* and *hard.* Ask them to write another word that could

be used in place of each of these words without changing the story's meaning.

3. Have students circle and write the story word contractions (it's, there's). Then have them write the words that comprise each contraction. Have students identify the homophones for *it's* and *there's* (its, theirs).

4. Have students research frog jumping contests, such as the Mark Twain Memorial in Hartford, Connecticut. Have them write a report about what they learn.

5. Have students circle and write the story word *catch.* Note the *tch* spelling. Have students find and write words that contain *tch* and *ch.* Conclude that the sound is the same, but the spelling is different.

DICTATION REVIEW 58

Materials: pencil, writing paper

Core Words

upon	286	later	288	move	290
family	287	turn	289		

Review Core Words

the (1), a (4), to (5), is (7), you (8), at (20), this (22), there (37), up (50), then (53), very (93), get (101), go (105), new (107), our (109), must (126), left (169), house (189), going (192), until (196), high (224), year (225), top (269), city (273)

Extra Words

pretty, hill, library, reach

Have students write the sentences as they are dictated. Provide assistance with the comma in the third sentence.

1. Our family is going to move later this year.
2. The new house is high upon a pretty hill.
3. To get there, you must turn left at the city library.
4. Then go up until you reach the very top.

■ Follow-Up Activity

Have students describe in writing the "dream house" they would like to move into this year with their family. Some students may wish to draw the house and its floor plan.

CLOZE STORY REVIEW 59

Materials: Master 59, pencil, writing paper

Core Words

face	291	cut	293	group	295
door	292	done	294		

Review Words

first (74), only (85), too (112), between (154), always (183), school (194), hand (223), second (235), white (239), example (261), turn (289)

Tell students that this story will help them tell the difference between facts and opinions. Read the story as students write the words. Then have students decide which story statement is a fact and which is an opinion. Next, students can write their opinion to answer the story question.

Fact or Opinion?

A fact is a statement that is (1) <u>always</u> true. On the other (2) <u>hand</u>, an opinion is something that a person or a (3) <u>group</u> believes, but isn't necessarily true. For (4) <u>example</u>, "the (5) <u>face</u> of George Washington is on the US dollar bill" is a fact. "(6) <u>White</u> is the (7) <u>only</u> color for the front (8) <u>door</u> to a (9) <u>school</u>," is an opinion. Now it's your (10) <u>turn</u> to decide which is which. (11) <u>First,</u> "it costs (12) <u>too</u> much to get your hair (13) <u>cut</u>." (14) <u>Second,</u> "night occurs when day is (15) <u>done</u>." Why is it important to know the difference (16) <u>between</u> facts and opinions? Write your opinion.

■ Extend Learning

1. Distinguish the factual statement from the opinion in the story. Then have students share their written opinions. Have students hypothesize what would be meant by the label, "an opinionated person."

2. Have students circle and write the story phrase *on the other hand* and discuss its idiomatic meaning. Explain the use of idioms in our language. Have students find and write more idioms.

3. Have students circle and write the story word *too*. Then have them write sentences that differentiate the two meanings for this word and its homophones, *two, to*.

4. Have students circle and write the story words *always, true, on, white, front, day*. Then have students write an antonym for each.

5. Have students predict the spellings through the word preview procedure of the review story words *something, it's, which, night* and the new story words *dollar, color, hair, isn't*. Have students check their predictions against the spelling of the story words.

DICTATION REVIEW 59

Materials: pencil, writing paper

Core Words

face	291	cut	293	group	295
door	292	done	294		

Review Core Words

the (1), and (3), to (5), that (9), it (10), was (13), be (21), I (24), all (33), would (59), my (80), down (84), after (94), back (103), go (105), right (116), want (193), hard (242), near (243), across (247), sure(ly) (251), knew (252), toward (275), didn't (281), morning (283), body (285), move (290)

Extra Words

inside, classroom, sat, speech

Have students write the sentences as they are dictated. Provide assistance with the comma in the last sentence.

1. I surely didn't want to face the group that morning.
2. It was hard to move my body toward the door to go inside.
3. I cut across the classroom and sat down near the back.
4. After my speech was done, I knew I would be all right.

■ Follow-Up Activity

Ask students to write advice for this person who is nervous about giving a speech. What might help this person become more comfortable giving a speech?

REVIEW 60 | Core Words 296–300

Use after Core Word 300

CLOZE STORY REVIEW 60

Materials: Master 60, pencil, art paper, crayons or colored markers

Core Words

true	296	red	298	plants	300
half	297	fish	299		

Review Words

there (37), their (42), many (55), its (76), through (102), animal(s) (207), above (213), country (228), picture (232), since (238), group (295)

This story will have you thinking about flags in a new way. Read the story as students write the words. Then have students divide into groups to develop a process for creating a flag. Then have students use the process to design one.

Flags

Flags have been waving (1) <u>through</u> history (2) <u>since</u> ancient times. They fly high (3) <u>above</u> buildings, on top of ships, and lead every parade (4) <u>there</u> ever was! Every (5) <u>country</u> and state creates (6) <u>its</u> own flag. Almost (7) <u>half</u> of them use a (8) <u>true</u> (9) <u>red</u> color in the design. Some (10) <u>picture</u> the body or head of (11) <u>animals</u>, birds, or (12) <u>fish</u>. Some show (13) <u>plants</u> or trees, or (14) <u>their</u> leaves or fruit. (15) <u>Many</u> feature the sun, moon, or stars. How would a (16) <u>group</u> create a flag to represent them? Divide into student sets of two or three and design your own flag.

■ Extend Learning

1. Have students share their process for deciding what would be a fitting flag for their group. Then ask them to show and tell about the flag they created.

2. Have students circle and write the story words *ancient, high, above, top, head, many*. Then have them write an antonym for each.

3. Have students circle and write the story word homophones. Choices may include *through, high, there, their, red, in, some, or, sun, you, would, to, two, its*. Then have students write their homophone partners.

4. Have interested students research flags to find one for each design named in the story. The information could be written and/or reported orally to the class.
5. Discuss the meaning of *true red*. Extend the discussion to *true friend*. Have students generalize in writing what could be said about any true friend.

DICTATION REVIEW 60

Materials: pencil, writing paper

Core Words

true	296	red	298	plants	300
half	297	fish	299		

Review Core Words

the (1), of (2), and (3), to (5), in (6), is (7), for (12), are (15), or (26), all (33), their (42), each (47), these (58), who (77), use (88), go (105), our (109), around (120), every (151), found (152), world (191), school (194), food (198), children (200), animal(s) (207), country (228), sentence(s) (244), answer (265)

Extra Words

false, girls, color, flag

Have students write the sentences as they are dictated.
1. Answer true or false to each of these sentences.
2. Half the children who go to our school are girls.
3. All animals use fish and plants for their food.
4. The color red is found in the flag of every country around the world.

■ Follow-Up Activity

Have students answer the sentence statements *true* or *false* and then explain their answers. Then have them write statements to which a friend can answer *true* or *false*.

REVIEW 61 Core Words 301-305

Use after Core Word 305

CLOZE STORY REVIEW 61

Materials: Master 61, pencil, writing paper

Core Words

living	301	eat	303	United States	305
black	302	short	304		

Review Words

about (48), use (88), after (94), along (171), life (208), high (224), story (237), white (239), across (247), hear (260), city (273)

Tell students that this story tells about some colorful places and things. Read the story as students write the words. Then have students continue writing the story.

Sailing Through Life with Flying Colors

Are you (1) <u>living</u> a colorful (2) <u>life</u> in the (3) <u>United States</u>? Do you live (4) <u>high</u> in the Blue Mountains, the (5) <u>Black</u> Hills, or on Grays Peak? Are you green with envy when you (6) <u>hear</u> they're painting the town red in the (7) <u>city</u> of Green Bay? Do you go (8) <u>white</u> water rafting (9) <u>along</u> the Red River or swim (10) <u>across</u> Red Lake? Do you (11) <u>use</u> the yellow pages? Are you tickled pink to (12) <u>eat</u> oranges (13) <u>after</u> school and have a "blue plate special" for dinner? Do you read (14) <u>short</u> mysteries (15) <u>about</u> Encyclopedia Brown? Can you add more to this (16) <u>story</u>?

■ Extend Learning

1. Have students share their story continuations.
2. Have students circle and write the *color* story words. Discuss *blue plate special* and *with flying colors* or other expressions that may be unfamiliar. If students are unfamiliar with Encyclopedia Brown, introduce them to Donald Sobol's mystery stories that feature this young detective.
3. Have students circle and write the story word proper nouns and explain why each is capitalized.
4. Have students circle and write the story word homophones. Choices may include *through, high, you, do, blue, or, peak, hear, they're, red, for, read, add, to.* Then have students write their homophone partners.

DICTATION REVIEW 61

Materials: pencil, writing paper

Core Words

living	301	eat	303	United States	305
black	302	short	304		

Review Core Words

the (1), of (2), and (3), a (4), to (5), in (6), is (7), you (8), on (14), are (15), what (32), we (36), can (38), which (41), each (47), about (48), two (65), could (70), way (86), find (87), most (99), write (108), part (129), name(s) (155), important (195), food (198), country (228), thing(s) (258), sea (267)

Extra Words

map, state(s), grows, provinces

Have students write the sentences as they are dictated.

1. Could you find the Black Sea on a map of the United States?
2. Which state grows most of the food we eat?
3. Can you name two important things about the part of the country in which you are living?
4. What is a short way to write the names of each of the states and provinces?

■ Follow-Up Activity

Have students write answers to the questions posed in the sentences. Conclude that the Black Sea is not in the United States, California grows more food than any other state, and the postal code abbreviations provide a short way to identify US states and Canadian provinces.

REVIEW 62 Core Words 306–310

Use after Core Word 310

CLOZE STORY REVIEW 62

Materials: Master 62, pencil, writing paper

Core Words

run	306	gave	308	open	310
book	307	order	309		

Review Words

were (34), their (42), about (48), these (58), find (87), such (133), important (195), food (198), life (208), told (255), living (301)

Tell students that this story is about the buffalo and will introduce them to another story about this distinctive beast. Read the story as students write the words. Then have students identify books available in your library that highlight the close ties between the Native Americans and the buffalo, as requested in the story question.

A Buffalo Tale

Years ago, buffalo herds (1) <u>were</u> a source of (2) <u>life</u> for the Native American people (3) <u>living</u> on the Great Plains. The tribes needed the buffalo in (4) <u>order</u> to live. First, the buffalo (5) <u>gave</u> the people (6) <u>food</u>. Then the buffalo hide was used in many (7) <u>important</u> ways, (8) <u>such</u> as for robes and tepee covers. The people were (9) <u>open</u> about (10) <u>their</u> respect for the beast. The native storytellers would never (11) <u>run</u> short of tales (12) <u>about</u> the glorious buffalo. One of (13) <u>these</u> stories is (14) <u>told</u> in the (15) <u>book</u> *Buffalo Woman* by Paul Goble. Can you (16) <u>find</u> others?

■ Extend Learning

1. Have students share their book lists that feature tales of the buffalo. Some students may be asked to write their own buffalo legends. Share with students the book *Buffalo Woman* by Paul Goble. Other books by Goble project a similar Native American theme, such as his Caldecott medal book, *The Girl Who Loved Wild Horses*. Goble is also the illustrator.

2. Discuss story words that may be unfamiliar, such as *Native American, Great Plains, respect, run short, glorious, buffalo hide, native storytellers, tepee.*

3. Have students find and circle each occurrence of *buffalo* in the story. Point out *buffalo* as the preferred plural spelling. Have students find buffalo in a dictionary and note the acceptable use of the plurals *oes/os.* Then have them find and write nouns that have the same singular and plural forms with no option for exceptions. Choices may include *bison, deer, grouse, moose, sheep, swine, trout, aircraft.*

4. Have students circle and write story words with more than one meaning. Choices may include *order, hide, run, short.*

DICTATION REVIEW 62

Materials: pencil, writing paper

Core Words

run	306	gave	308	open	310
book(s)	307	order	309		

Review Core Words

the (1), of (2), to (5), in (6), you (8), for (12),
be (21), were (34), an (39), their (42), how (49),
them (52), then (53), she (54), her (64), first (74),
find (87), right (116), must (126), old (144),
asked (188), told (255), whole (259), answer (265),
morning (283), group (295), United States (305)

Extra Words

teacher, students, question, President

Have students write the sentences as they are
dictated. Provide assistance with the comma in the
second sentence.

1. In the morning, the teacher gave the whole group
   an order.
2. First, the students were told to open their books.
3. Then she asked them to find the right answer to
   her question.
4. How old must you be to run for President of the
   United States?

■ **Follow-Up Activity**

Have students research and write the answer to the
sentence question. Conclude that one qualification for
the presidency is to be thirty-five years old. Have
students find and write other presidential qualifications.

REVIEW 63 Core Words 311–315

Use after Core Word 315

CLOZE STORY REVIEW 63

Materials: Master 63, pencil, writing paper

Core Words

ground	311	really	313	remember	315
cold	312	table	314		

Review Words

they (19), your (40), some (56), first (74),
people (79), called (96), because (127), until (196),
learn (271), morning (283), United States (305)

Tell students that this story will make them smell a
favorite breakfast. Read the story as students write
the words. Then have students describe in writing the
aroma of piping hot pancakes with maple syrup, or
any other favorite breakfast treat.

A Breakfast Treat

On a (1) cold winter (2) morning when the
(3) ground is covered with snow, it's (4) really a
treat to have piping hot pancakes! Can you
(5) remember the smell of the maple syrup at
(6) your breakfast (7) table? Maple syrup comes
from the sugar maple tree. Native Americans
(8) called it "maple water" (9) because it dripped
from the tree as sap. (10) They were the (11) first to
(12) learn how to boil the sap (13) until it became
sweet syrup. Now the production of the syrup is a
big industry for (14) people in (15) some parts of
the (16) United States, as well as in Canada.

■ **Extend Learning**

1. Have students share their written descriptions
   of breakfast aromas. Follow up with students
   gathering advertisements of breakfast foods and
   identifying the language used to describe good
   morning taste treats.
2. Ask students to research which states produce
   maple syrup. Conclude that the maple syrup-
   producing states are IL, IN, ME, MD, MA, MI,
   NH, NY, OH, VT, and WI.
3. Have students circle and write the story word *it's*.
   Then have them write six sentences using either
   it's or *its*. Next, have students read their sentences
   to a partner who must identify which homophone
   is being used.
4. Have students circle and write the story word
   compounds *pancakes* and *breakfast*. Discuss the
   pancake synonyms *hotcakes* and *flapjacks*. Then
   have students circle and write the story word *water*.
   Ask students to create *water____* compounds.
   Choices may include *watercolor, waterfall,
   waterfront, waterlily, watermelon, waterpower,
   waterproof, waterway*. Discuss the meanings of the
   words and the spelling options different dictionaries
   offer, such as *waterski* or *water ski*.

DICTATION REVIEW 63

Materials: pencil, writing paper

Core Words

ground	311	really	313	remember	315
cold	312	table	314		

Review Core Words

the (1), of (2), and (3), it (10), was (13), on (14), one (28), had (29), when (35), there (37), about (48), so (57), two (65), could (70), no (71), been (75), new (107), around (120), still (153), feet (201), almost (216), hard (242), several (263)

Extra Words

friends, sat, talking, weather, snow(ing), blowing

Have students write the sentences as they are dictated.

1. Several friends sat around the table talking about the weather.
2. No one could remember when it had been so cold.
3. It was still snowing and blowing really hard.
4. There was almost two feet of new snow on the ground.

■ **Follow-Up Activity**

Have students write about the coldest or hottest weather they can remember. Then have them tell what was good and bad about that day.

REVIEW 64 Core Words 316–320

Use after Core Word 320

CLOZE STORY REVIEW

Materials: Master 64, pencil, writing paper

Core Words

| tree | 316 | front | 318 | space | 320 |
| course | 317 | American | 319 | | |

Review Words

what (32), which (41), its (76), because (127), great (146), own (163), might (173), want (193), usually (278), family (287), table (314)

Tell students that this story will get them thinking about the fun they've had at past holidays. Read the story as students write the words. Then have students write their answer to the story question, stating reasons why their choice is best.

A Favorite Holiday

(1) <u>Which</u> holiday is your favorite? Thanksgiving, the oldest (2) <u>American</u> holiday, is (3) <u>usually</u> celebrated around the dinner (4) <u>table</u>. Of (5) <u>course</u>, Independence Day is a (6) <u>great</u> day for (7) <u>family</u> picnics. You (8) <u>might</u> choose Christmas (9) <u>because</u> it's fun to decorate the (10) <u>tree</u> and place it in (11) <u>front</u> of a window for all to see. If you observe Hanukkah, you may (12) <u>want</u> to choose it. (13) <u>What</u> about Halloween with (14) <u>its</u> costumes that transform people into such things as (15) <u>space</u> rangers and ghosts? Or your (16) <u>own</u> birthday may be the best day of all!

■ **Extend Learning**

1. Have students share their answers to the story question. Discuss the holidays in the story and their meaning. Record students' favorite holidays on the chalkboard and have students graph the results. Then have them interpret the graph in writing.

2. Ask students to research which two holidays are the only "national holidays" in America (Thanksgiving, Independence Day). Then have them find out which holidays are proclaimed by their state or province. Have students write why the Fourth of July is celebrated in the United States, but not in Canada (it is America's Independence Day). Then have them name which day is a similar day of celebration in Canada (July 1).

3. Have students circle and write the story words *which, dinner, choose, its, costumes, your.* Then have students contrast these words with *witch, diner, chose, it's, customs, you're.* Have students write the words in sentences to help differentiate them.

4. Have students circle and write the story words with double letters.

5. Have students circle and write the story words *holiday* and *family.* Then have them find and write ten more words that end in vowel-y and consonant-y. Have students write their plural forms. Next, ask students to write the rule for forming the plurals of words ending in vowel-y (add s) and consonant-y (change y to i and add es).

DICTATION REVIEW 64

Materials: pencil, writing paper

Core Words

tree	316	front	318	space	320
course	317	American	319		

Review Core Words

the (1), of (2), you (8), on (14), they (19), this (22), or (26), one (28), were (34), we (36), about (48), up (50), them (52), into (61), than (73), who (77), new(s) (107), write (108), any (113), day (114), went (143), name (155), large (185), don't (190), page (218), high(er) (224), story (237), sure (251), learn(ed) (271), I'm (284), remember (315)

Extra Words

astronauts, building, person, flight

Have students write the sentences as they are dictated.

1. We learned about American astronauts who went into space.
2. Of course, they were up higher than any large tree or building.
3. I'm sure you remember the name of one of them, don't you?
4. Write the front page news story about this person on the day of the flight.

■ Follow-Up Activity

Have students research an astronaut to answer the question posed in the third sentence. Then have them write the news story requested in sentence four.

REVIEW 65 Core Words 321–325

Use after Core Word 325

CLOZE STORY REVIEW 65

Materials: Master 65, pencil, writing paper

Core Words

inside	321	sad	323	I'll	325
ago	322	early	324		

Review Words

there (37), each (47), than (73), only (85), through (102), thought (179), until (196), several (263), answer (265), later (288), really (313), remember (315)

Tell students that this is a riddle story. Read the story as students write the words. Then have students write their answer to the story riddle.

Measure Your Thinking Ability

A long time (1) <u>ago</u>, my mother gave me a book of riddles, but the (2) <u>answer</u> page was gone from (3) <u>inside</u> of it. (4) <u>Several</u> of the riddles were easy, however, (5) <u>there</u> was one that (6) <u>really</u> stumped me. (7) <u>Early</u> one morning I read the riddle and (8) <u>thought</u> about it (9) <u>through</u> the day. I was (10) <u>sad</u> until I finally solved the puzzle (11) <u>later</u> that night. Can you figure it out? "What has a foot on (12) <u>each</u> side and one in the middle?" (13) <u>Remember</u>, some words have more (14) <u>than</u> one meaning. That's the (15) <u>only</u> hint (16) <u>I'll</u> give you. Just keep trying (17) <u>until</u> you have it!

■ Extend Learning

1. Have students share their answers to the story riddle. Conclude that a yardstick is the solution. Then have students find and write another riddle for their classmates to solve. Compile the riddles into a class book.

2. Ask students to circle and write the story words that have more than one meaning. Choices may include *long, page, through, foot, side, can, figure, time.* Discuss the different meanings.

3. Have students circle and write the story words *mother, answer, inside, several, easy, early, morning, day, sad, later, night, more.* Then have students write an antonym for each.

4. Have students circle and write the story words *thought* and *through.* Have them underline the *ough.* Then have them find and write more words with *ough,* such as *enough, brought, though, bought, although, throughout, rough.* The *ou* is the most deviant vowel combination in English spelling and often causes spelling errors.

DICTATION REVIEW 65

Materials: pencil, writing paper

Core Words

inside	321	sad	323	I'll	325
ago	322	early	324		

Review Core Words

the (1), and (3), a (4), to (5), that (9), it (10), I (24), one (28), not (30), some (56), would (59), like (66), my (80), made (81), long (91), me (110), day (114), again (141), read(ing) (165), both (180), always (183), began (215), father (229), night (231), story (237), morning (283), later (288), book (307), gave (308), remember (315)

Extra Words

super, finished, feel, happy

Have students write the sentences as they are dictated.

1. Not long ago, my father gave me a super book.
2. I began reading it early one morning and finished it later that night.
3. I'll always remember the story and would like to read it again some day.
4. It made me feel both happy and sad inside.

■ Follow-Up Activity

Have students identify a book, movie, TV show, or play that made them feel both happy and sad. Ask them to explain in writing why it made them feel that way.

REVIEW 66 Core Words 326–330
Use after Core Word 330

CLOZE STORY REVIEW 66

Materials: Master 66, pencil, art paper, old magazines, glue, scissors

Core Words

learned	326	close	328	though	330
brought	327	nothing	329		

Review Words

its (76), use (88), too (112), different (139), together (187), head (212), paper (241), today (249), body (285), turn (289), face (291)

Tell students that this story will introduce them to some crazy characters. Read the story as students write the words. Then have students create their cut-out characters.

Crazy Cut-Out Characters

(1) <u>Today</u> I made a cut-out. First, I (2) <u>brought</u> (3) <u>together</u> all the things I'd need—a pencil, glue, (4) <u>paper</u>, and scissors. First, I drew a big circle for a (5) <u>head</u>. I had old magazines (6) <u>close</u> by to (7) <u>use</u> for cut outs. Next, I cut out (8) <u>different</u> colored eyes, large ears, and a bright red mouth. I glued them on the circle to make a funny (9) <u>face</u>. Even (10) <u>though</u> my cut-up person was looking very silly, I (11) <u>learned</u> that (12) <u>nothing</u> was (13) <u>too</u> foolish. I glued (14) <u>its</u> legs and arms to a (15) <u>body</u>. Last, I put on two fish for feet! Now it's your (16) <u>turn</u> to make a very crazy cut-out!

■ Extend Learning

1. Have students share their cut-out characters. Discuss the colloquial meaning of *cut-up*. Then have students write a character description of their crazy character to staple to its body for display on a bulletin board.

2. Ask students to circle and write story word homographs *use* and *close*. Discuss their different pronunciations and meanings. Then have students write each word in a sentence that uses the meaning that was not used in the story.

3. Have students circle and write the story words *to, two, too, its, it's*. Have students explain in writing how they know when to use each homophone. Then have them circle and write more story word homophones. Choices may include *I, made, I'd, by, for, red, very, feet*.

4. Have students reread the story and note the sequence of events. Then have them write another how-to sequence of events. Provide suggestions for a topic that has definite steps toward completion.

DICTATION REVIEW 66

Materials: pencil, writing paper

Core Words

learned	326	close	328	though	330
brought	327	nothing	329		

Review Core Words

the (1), of (2), a (4), to (5), in (6), you (8), it (10), on (14), as (16), I (24), when (35), can (38), my (80), down (84), use (88), may (89), water (90), back (103), look (117), think (118), come (123), away (140), never (167), along (171), large (185), once (206), head (212), second (235), soon (236), whole (259), sea (267), body (285), turn (289), ground (311)

Extra Words

I've, I'm, I'd, wave(s)

Have students write the sentences as they are dictated. Provide assistance with the comma in the second sentence.

1. I've learned to use my head when I'm close to the sea.
2. Though you may think nothing of it, I'd never turn my back on the water.
3. Large waves can come along as soon as you look away.
4. Once a wave brought my whole body down to the ground in a second.

■ **Follow-Up Activity**

Have students identify another water safety tip. Have them write the water safety idea and tell why they think it's an important one.

REVIEW 67 | Core Words 331–335

Use after Core Word 335

CLOZE STORY REVIEW 67

Materials: Master 67, pencil, writing paper

Core Words

| idea | 331 | lived | 333 | add | 335 |
| before | 332 | became | 334 | | |

Review Words

of (2), what (32), said (43), people (79), off (142), every (151), until (196), seen (280), didn't (281), learned (326), though (330)

Tell students that this story will introduce them to an inventor who built something they know well. Read the story as students write the words. Then have students write their answer to the story question.

A Contraption Becomes an Invention

(1) <u>People</u> laughed at Kirkpatrick Macmillan's (2) <u>idea</u>. A silly contraption he was making (3) <u>became</u> the town joke. Never (4) <u>before</u> had anyone (5) <u>seen</u> anything like it. It had two big wheels with a seat. Macmillan (6) <u>said</u> he planned to ride it. Even (7) <u>though</u> he fell or hit something (8) <u>every</u> time he tried to ride the thing, he (9) <u>didn't</u> give up. He (10) <u>learned</u> that he had to (11) <u>add</u> a brake. When the wheels came (12) <u>off</u>, he made them stronger. He (13) <u>lived</u> a life (14) <u>of</u> trial and error (15) <u>until</u> his invention finally worked. (16) <u>What</u> do you suppose he invented?

■ **Extend Learning**

1. Have students share their answers to the story question. The invention was the bicycle, invented in Scotland in 1830. Ask interested students to research Macmillan and his invention.

2. Ask students to circle and write the story word *contraption*. Discuss its meaning. Then write the word *contraction* on the chalkboard. Have students find and write a story word contraction (didn't). Have students in a timed activity (about three minutes) list contractions. Then make a cumulative class list on the chalkboard.

3. Have students circle and write the story words *of* and *off*. Contrast the words. Then have students circle and write story words *though, trial,* and *finally*. Contrast these with *through, thought, thorough,* and *trail,* and *finely*. Discuss the meaning of *trial and error*.

4. Have students circle and write the story words *laughed, planned, tried, learned, made, lived, worked, invented*. Then have students write the other word forms of these past tense verbs.

5. Have students predict the spellings through the word preview procedure of the review story words *something, it's, which, night* and the new story words *dollar, color, hair, isn't*. Have students check their predictions against the spelling of the story words.

DICTATION REVIEW 67

Materials: pencil, writing paper

Core Words

idea 331	lived 333	add 335
before 332	became 334	

Review Core Words

the (1), of (2), and (3), to (5), it (10), was (13), are (15), I (24), how (49), would (59), my (80), through (102), even (130), never (167), something (178), began (215), body (285), cold (312), remember (315)

Extra Words

math, test(s), easy, fun

Tell students that one of the sentences has a comma. Have students write the sentences as they are dictated.
1. I lived through my math test and it was easy!
2. Before the test began, my body became cold.
3. Would I even remember how to add?
4. Tests are never my idea of something fun.

■ Follow-Up Activity

Have students write about a time when they felt as uncomfortable before a test as the person in the sentences. Then later they discovered that they had nothing to fear. Discuss how the fear of something is usually far worse than the event.

REVIEW 68 Core Words 336–340
Use after Core Word 340

CLOZE STORY REVIEW 68

Materials: Master 68, pencil, writing paper

Core Words

become 336	draw 338	less 340
grow 337	yet 339	

Review Words

then (53), would (59), than (73), words (95), write (108), try (254), family (287), really (313), course (317), ago (322), learned (326)

Tell students that this story tells about an ancient way to communicate. Read the story as students write the words. Then have students research picture languages and write about one thing they learned.

Picture Language

If you wanted to (1) <u>write</u> a story for your friends and (2) <u>family</u>, but letters of the alphabet hadn't been invented, how (3) <u>would</u> you do it? (4) <u>Draw</u> the story! (5) <u>Yet</u>, it's easy to (6) <u>become</u> frustrated and (7) <u>grow</u> angry as you (8) <u>try</u> to create pictures that say what you (9) <u>really</u> mean. Long (10) <u>ago</u>, written language was mainly pictures, but of (11) <u>course</u> it was far (12) <u>less</u> effective (13) <u>than</u> reading the message in (14) <u>words</u>. Research *ancient picture languages*. Look up *pictograph* and *hieroglyphics*. (15) <u>Then</u> write one thing you (16) <u>learned</u>.

■ Extend Learning

1. By looking up *pictograph* and *hieroglyphics* in the media center, students will be led to information on ancient picture languages. Have them share their research orally and/or in writing. Follow up with students trying to express a message with pictures . . . and then in writing.
2. Ask students to circle and write the story words *friend, angry, ancient*. Then have them write a synonym for each. Discuss the meaning of the phrases *become frustrated* and *less effective*.
3. Have students circle and write the story words that use *ea* to spell the *long e* sound (speak, read, each, easy, really, mean, reading). Then have them find and write more words with this spelling pattern.
4. Have students circle and write the story word *picture*. Then have them write a sentence using the word as a noun and another as a verb. Contrast *picture* with *pitcher*.
5. Have students circle and write the story words *then* and *than*. Have them write a sentence using each word. Expand the lesson to *picture/pitcher, message/massage, our/are, later/latter, quit/quiet, thorough/through/though*.

DICTATION REVIEW 68

Materials: pencil, writing paper

Core Words

become 336	draw 338	less 340
grow 337	yet 339	

Review Core Words

a (4), to (5), with (17), this (22), I (24), not (30), when (35), up (50), make (72), than (73), my (80), after (94), good (106), me (110), day (114), work (124), even (130), great (146), every (151), want (193,) school (194), important (195), enough (209), picture(s) (232), best (246), it's (253), play (274), toward (275), I'm (284), though (330)

Extra Words

artist, outside, fun, friends

Tell students that two of the sentences have a comma. Have students write the sentences as they are dictated.

1. I want to become a great artist when I grow up.
2. Even though I work toward this every day, I'm not good enough yet.
3. It's less important to me to play outside than to draw.
4. After school, it's fun to make pictures with my best friends.

■ Follow-Up Activity

Have students find out about the Caldecott award that honors the most outstanding picture book each year. Then have them identify one winner and write about its illustrator.

REVIEW 69   Core Words 341–345

Use after Core Word 345

CLOZE STORY REVIEW 69

Materials: Master 69, pencil, writing paper

Core Words

wind	341	cannot	343	among	345
behind	342	letter	344		

Review Words

there (37), which (41), its (76), through (102), also (119), even (130), something (178), few (181), several (263), front (318), yet (339)

Tell students that this story points out how communication has changed. Read the story as students write the words. Then have students write their answer to the story question.

Kite Communication

Today, (1) there are (2) several ways of communicating with someone from afar. You might write a (3) letter, send a FAX, use a computer online system, or call on a telephone. Long ago, kites sent messages. The way a kite flew (4) through the (5) wind, the kite's color, and (6) its shape were (7) among the ways kites communicated. (8) Also, the way in (9) which kites flew in (10) front of and (11) behind each other meant (12) something. (13) Yet, kite communication had a (14) few problems that (15) even modern kites (16) cannot overcome. What difficulties are these?

■ Extend Learning

1. Have students share their answer to the story question. Then have them write or tell about the variety of kites available today.
2. Have students circle and write the story word homophones. Choices may include *there, ways, you, might, write, or, flew, through*.
3. Have students write the story word compounds *someone, something, cannot, overcome, online, today*. Then have students find and write more compound words.
4. Have students circle and write the story words *several, afar, might, cannot, difficulties*. Then have students substitute a synonym for these words that would not change the story meaning.
5. Have students predict the spellings through the word preview procedure of the review story words *from, might, write, these* and the new story words *kite, computer, telephone, color*. Have students check their predictions against the spelling of the story words.

DICTATION REVIEW 69

Materials: pencil, writing paper

Core Words

wind	341	cannot	343	among	345
behind	342	letter	344		

Review Core Words

the (1), of (2), and (3), a (4), to (5), it (10), was (13), I (24), there (37), out (51), some (56), see (68), now (78), my (80), find (87), get (101), me (110), around (120), came (122), because (127), help (137), along (171), saw (177), important (195), took (210), need (221), hand (223), however (250), sure (251), didn't (281), turn(ed) (289), cannot (343)

Extra Words

strong, blow, autumn, leaves, anywhere

Tell students that one of the sentences has commas. Have students write the sentences as they are dictated.

1. A strong wind came along and took the important letter out of my hand.
2. I was sure I saw it blow among some autumn leaves behind me.
3. I turned around to get it, however, I didn't see it there.
4. Now I need some help because I cannot find it anywhere.

■ **Follow-Up Activity**

Have students describe in writing ways the wind can cause difficulties and ways it can be helpful.

REVIEW 70 Core Words 346–350

Use after Core Word 350

CLOZE STORY REVIEW 70

Materials: Master 70, pencil, art paper, colored crayons or markers

Core Words

able	346	shown	348	English	350
dog	347	mean	349		

Review Words

another (121), because (127), does (128), picture (232), sentence (244), it's (253), example(s) (261), really (313), idea (331), draw (338), among (345)

Tell students that this is a "thumbs up" story for "eager beavers" who want to "jump on the bandwagon" and use their "gray matter." Discuss these idiomatic expressions. Then read the story as

students write the words. Discuss the meaning of the title and the story idiom. Then have students think of another idiom and draw two pictures to show the literal meaning and then the intended meaning.

Watch Out for Idioms!

Knowing (1) <u>English</u> words (2) <u>does</u> not guarantee that you'll be (3) <u>able</u> to understand the language. This is (4) <u>because</u> people use *idioms*. Idioms are words that say one thing, but (5) <u>mean</u> something else. (6) <u>Among</u> the many (7) <u>examples</u> would be this (8) <u>sentence:</u> "This TV series is a (9) <u>dog</u>!" If this comment gives you the (10) <u>idea</u> that a poodle or other canine will be (11) <u>shown</u> in this TV show, you're wrong! Think of an idiom. Then, (12) <u>draw</u> one (13) <u>picture</u> to show what (14) <u>it's</u> actually saying and (15) <u>another</u> to show what it (16) <u>really</u> intended to say.

■ **Extend Learning**

1. Have students show their two pictures while the class writes which idiom they think is being pictured. Then discuss the idiom.
2. Have students find and circle the story word *canine*. Discuss how context can help the reader understand an unfamiliar word. Demonstrate with the clue word *poodle*.
3. Have students circle and write the story words *other* and *another* for comparison.
4. Have students circle and write the story word contractions (you'll, you're, it's). Then have them create a contraction in the story by using two consecutive story words (does not, doesn't).
5. Have students find and circle *TV* in the story. Then have them write its longer form (television). Have students list other examples of letters that we use for shortcuts. Choices may include CD (compact disc), DJ (disc jockey), BLT (bacon-lettuce-tomato sandwich), and FAX (facsimile, used in Review 69).

DICTATION REVIEW 70

Materials: pencil, writing paper

Core Words

able	346	shown	348	English	350
dog	347	mean	349		

Review Core Words

of (2), and (3), to (5), is (7), you (8), that (9), they (19), be (21), what (32), we (36), said (43), do (45), them (52), then (53), our (109), must (126), such (133), us (168), something (178), animal(s) (207), told (255), thing(s) (258), heard (262), change(d) (264), usually (278), course (317), cannot (343)

Extra Words

pet, speak, laughed, mind

Review use of punctuation for dialogue. Have students write the sentences as they are dictated.

1. "Our pet dog is able to speak English," they said to us.
2. We laughed and told them, "We must be shown what you mean."
3. Of course, animals cannot usually do such things.
4. Then we heard something that changed our mind.

■ Follow-Up Activity

Have students write what happened next to finish the story. Then have them tell about an animal that can really do something unusual.

REVIEW 71 Core Words 351–355

Use after Core Word 355

CLOZE STORY REVIEW 71

Materials: Master 71, pencil, writing paper

Core Words

rest	351	certain	353	feel	355
perhaps	352	six	354		

Review Words

there (37), their (42), then (53), than (73), most (99), true (296), United States (305), cold (312), American(s) (319), though (330), behind (342)

Tell students that this story is about a favorite dessert. Read the story as students write the words. Then have students do their ice cream cone research and report their findings in writing.

Scream for Ice Cream

(1) <u>Americans</u> love ice cream! (2) <u>There</u> is more ice cream eaten in the (3) <u>United States</u> (4) <u>than</u> in any country in the (5) <u>rest</u> of the world. A (6) <u>certain</u> favorite is the ice cream sundae. (7) <u>Most</u> historians (8) <u>feel</u> that this dessert was named for Sunday, even (9) <u>though</u> the two words are spelled differently. After people worked hard for (10) <u>six</u> days, (11) <u>then</u> the seventh day was for enjoying (12) <u>their</u> "sundae." (13) <u>Perhaps</u> the greatest invention to increase the popularity of this (14) <u>cold</u> treat was the ice cream cone. Explore the (15) <u>true</u> story (16) <u>behind</u> this super discovery.

■ Extend Learning

1. Have students share their findings about the invention of the ice cream cone. Confirm that the first ice cream cone was served at the 1904 St. Louis World's Fair. An ice cream vendor ran out of serving dishes and the waffle vendor next to him offered his waffles as a substitute.
2. Have students circle and write the story words *than* and *then*. Contrast these often-confused words. Have students circle the story words *country, dessert, though, are, super*. Contrast these words with *county, desert, through, our, supper*.
3. Have students circle and write the story homophones *there/their* and *Sunday/sundae*. Ask students to write the words in sentences. Then have them write the homophone partners for the story words *week, two, days*.
4. Have students create a menu for an ice cream sundae shop with delicious descriptions of the sundae treats.
5. Have students write the abbreviations for the United States of America, the days of the week, the months of the year, and the Canadian provinces.

DICTATION REVIEW 71

Materials: pencil, writing paper

Core Words

rest	351	certain	353	feel	355
perhaps	352	six	354		

Review Core Words

the (1), of (2), and (3), a (4), to (5), in (6),
you (8), are (15), one (28), there (37), can (38),
your (40), which (41), them (52), she (54),
like (66), most (99), write (108), put (138),
often (186), food(s) (198), mother (226),
sure (251), I'm (284), eat (303), order (309)

Extra Words

choose, favorites, list, ask, taste

Have students write the sentences as they are dictated.

1. I'm sure there are certain foods that you like to eat often.
2. Choose your six favorites and write them in a list.
3. Ask your mother which one she feels you like most.
4. Perhaps she can put the rest in order of your taste.

■ **Follow-Up Activity**

Have students complete the experiment with their mother or another relative or friend. Then have students explain how well the person ordered the foods by preference.

REVIEW 72 — Core Words 356–360

Use after Core Word 360

CLOZE STORY REVIEW 72

Materials: Master 72, pencil, writing paper

Core Words

fire	356	green	358	built	360
ready	357	yes	359		

Review Words

there (37), their (42), first (74), always (183),
together (187), form (197), animal (207),
ground (311), front (318), become (336),
mean(s) (349)

Tell students that this story describes the construction of a special kind of house. Read the story as students write the words. Then have students hypothesize in writing why the tepee door always faced east.

Making a Tepee

The word tepee (1) <u>means</u> "for living in." The (2) <u>first</u> tepees were (3) <u>built</u> by Native Americans of the Great Plains. To make one, tall trees were cut and stripped of (4) <u>their</u> (5) <u>green</u> leaves and branches to (6) <u>become</u> poles. Three large poles were put (7) <u>together</u> to (8) <u>form</u> a tripod. Next, (9) <u>animal</u> hides were (10) <u>ready</u> to be attached to the poles and fastened to the (11) <u>ground</u>. A smoke hole was made at the top for venting the inside (12) <u>fire</u>. A flap for the (13) <u>front</u> door (14) <u>always</u> faced east. (15) <u>Yes</u>, (16) <u>there</u> was a good reason for doing this. Can you explain why?

■ **Extend Learning**

1. Have students share their answers to the story question. Conclude that the door faced east for two main reasons. First, the morning sun, rising in the East, could bring heat and light to the tepee. Second, the wind and weather usually came from the West, so this side of the home was best protected by a solid covering.
2. Note that the Native Americans spelled tepee, *tipi*. Occasionally students may see it spelled this way.
3. Have students circle and write the story homophones. Choices may include *for, in, by, great, to, one, their, be, hole, made, there, you*. Then have them write their homophone partners.
4. Have students circle and write the story words *first, large, together, top, inside, front, always, east, yes, good*. Then have students write their antonyms.
5. Have students predict the spellings through the word preview procedure of the review story words *next, large, door, trees, inside* and the new story words *hole, east, leaves, reason*. Have students check their predictions against the spelling of the story words.

DICTATION REVIEW 72

Materials: pencil, writing paper

Core Words

fire	356	green	358	built	360
ready	357	yes	359		

Review Core Words

of (2), and (3), a (4), your (8), he (11), for (12), are (15), be (21), all (33), were (34), there (37), your (40), would (59), my (80), our (109), around (120), us (168), large (185), asked (188), father (229), knew (252), answer (265), against (268), tree(s) (316), course (317)

Extra Words

tall, fir, campground (ground 311), rock, dinner, friends

Review use of punctuation for dialogue. Have students write the sentences as they are dictated.

1. There were tall green fir trees all around our campground.
2. My father built a fire against a large rock.
3. "Are you ready for your dinner?" he asked us and our friends.
4. Of course, he knew our answer would be yes.

■ Follow-Up Activity

Have students make a list of ten things that a camper must remember to take on a camping trip. Then have students share their lists.

REVIEW 73   Core Words 361–365

Use after Core Word 365

CLOZE STORY REVIEW 73

Materials: Master 73, pencil, writing paper

Core Words

special	361	full	363	complete	365
ran	362	town	364		

Review Words

its (76), every (151), along (171), next (174), often (186), city (273), early (324), nothing (329), yet (339), certain(ly) (353), fire (356)

Tell students that this story tells about telling time in the early days. Read the story as students write the words. Then have students hypothesize the problems that the users of candle clocks might encounter.

What Time Is It?

In the (1) early days, the (2) town bell was a (3) special signal to tell the time. (4) Every hour on the hour, a bell ringer (5) ran up the bell tower to ring the bell. At noon and midnight, it rang a (6) full twelve times. (7) Yet, the bells did (8) nothing for those who lived far from the (9) city. Country people (10) often told time by the sun, but some people used candle clocks. The candle had marks (11) along (12) its side. A (13) complete hour had passed when the (14) fire burned from one mark to the (15) next. (16) Certainly, these clocks had a few problems. Explain these limitations.

■ Extend Learning

1. Have students share their limitations of the candle clocks. Then have students work in pairs or small groups to list different time-keeping devices that have helped people tell time in the past or today. Choices may include a wall clock, digital clock, cuckoo clock, grandmother or grandfather clock, kitchen timer, stop watch, pocket watch, sundial, hourglass.

2. Have students circle and write two sets of story word antonyms (city/country, noon/midnight). Then have students circle and write the story words *early, up, on, nothing, often.* Then have students write an antonym for each.

3. Have students circle and write the story word *along.* Then have them write *a long.* Discuss the difference. Then discuss *a head/ahead, a part/apart, a way/away, a cross/across.* Have students write the words in sentences to differentiate these look-alike words.

4. Have students circle and write the story word *certainly.* Discuss *certain* and its *ly* suffix. Have students circle and write the story words *special, hour, time, complete.* Then have them add the *ly* suffix to each and discuss the meaning and use of the new words.

DICTATION REVIEW 73

Materials: pencil, writing paper

Core Words

special	361	full	363	complete	365
ran	362	town	364		

Review Core Words

the (1), of (2), a (4), to (5), as (16), at (20),
their (42), them (52), many (55), some (56),
other(s) (60), people (79), only (85), water (90),
through (102), go (105), off (142), went (143),
along (171), large (185), keep (199), far (222),
during (248), whole (259), turned (270),
point (272), group (295), half (297), run (306),
course (317), brought (327), certain (353)

Extra Words

runners, distance, race, cool

Have students write the sentences as they are dictated.

1. The large group of runners ran through the town
   along a special course.
2. Some went the full distance to complete the
   whole race.
3. Others turned off at a certain point to go only
   half as far.
4. Many people brought them water during their
   run to keep them cool.

■ Follow-Up Activity

Have students list sporting competitions in which
participants may compete as individuals, rather than
on a team, such as running track or cross country.
Then have them list team sports.

REVIEW 74 Core Words 366–370

Use after Core Word 370

CLOZE STORY REVIEW 74

Materials: Master 74, pencil, writing paper

Core Words

oh	366	hot	368	hold	370
person	367	anything	369		

Review Words

there (37), their (42), because (127), always (183),
important (195), sure (251), turned (270), half (297),
remember (315), special (361), complete (365)

Tell students that this story tells about safety. Read
the story as students write the words. Then have
students make a list of kitchen safety tips.

Safety in the Kitchen

Safety is (1) important. For example, you must
(2) remember to take (3) special care when you are
in the kitchen preparing food. Almost (4) anything
in this room can be dangerous if it is not used
correctly. Over (5) half the kitchen accidents occur
(6) because of careless use of knives. Do you
(7) hold all (8) hot pots with a pot holder?
(9) Always be (10) sure pot handles are (11) turned
to the back or side of the stove so (12) their handles
cannot be bumped by a (13) person walking by.
(14) underline{Oh}, (15) there are a lot more safety ideas!
Make a (16) complete kitchen safety list.

■ Extend Learning

1. Have students share their lists. Then have
   students brainstorm other times when safety
   is particularly important, such as safety for
   pedestrians or skiers. Have students work in
   pairs to create additional safety lists.
2. Have students circle and write the story words
   there and *their*. Discuss *they're*. Then have
   students write these words in sentences.
3. Have students circle and write the story words
   always and *almost*. Compare these words with *all
   right* and *a lot*. Have students circle and write the
   story words *a lot*.
4. Have students circle and write the story words
   food and *room*. Then in a timed write (about three
   minutes) have students find and write more words
   with *oo*, such as *good, too, school, book, blood,
   door*. Note that the *oo* makes different sounds
   in words.
5. Have students circle and write the story words *it
   is, cannot,* and *you are*. Have students make these
   words into contractions.

DICTATION REVIEW 74

Materials: pencil, writing paper

Core Words

oh	366	hot	368	hold	370
person	367	anything	369		

Review Core Words

the (1), a(4), to (5), in (6), is (7), you (8), it (10), are (15), they (19), or (26), but (31), all (33), some (56), like(s) (66), who (77), people (79), right (116), old(er) (144), say (149), often (186), until (196), children (200), let (230), however, (250), try (254), young (256), sun (257), usually (278), cold (312)

Extra Words

weather, snow, onto, summer, late, fall, shout

Have students write the sentences as they are dictated.

1. Are you a person who likes cold or hot weather?
2. Some older people often say anything is all right, but snow.
3. They try to hold onto the summer sun until late in the fall.
4. However, young children usually shout, "Oh, let it snow!"

■ Follow-Up Activity

Have students hypothesize why younger people often want the snow to fall, but some older people do not welcome the snow. Ask them to offer their explanation in writing, stating reasons for their opinion.

REVIEW 75 Core Words 371-375

Use after Core Word 375

CLOZE STORY REVIEW

Materials: Master 75, pencil, writing paper

Core Words

state	371	stood	373	ten	375
list	372	hundred	374		

Review Words

first (74), water (90), go(es) (105), great (146), form(ed) (197), until (196), almost (216), several (263), answer (265), later (288), built (360)

Tell students that this is a puzzle story. Read the story as students write the words. Then have students write an answer to the title question and hypothesize why this age-old building material has withstood time as a building material.

What Are They?

The Empire (1) State Building was (2) built with (3) ten million of them. The (4) Great Wall of China stretches fifteen (5) hundred miles and contains (6) almost four million. Their (7) list of famous uses (8) goes on! The (9) first ones were probably (10) formed by ancient Egyptians from mud that (11) stood in the sun (12) until it was dry. (13) Later it was cut into blocks. Now they're made from mined clay mixed with (14) water to make a goo that's shaped and baked in hot ovens. A Johnson City, Tennessee museum displays (15) several notable old ones. Now (16) answer the story title.

■ Extend Learning

1. Have students share their answers to the story title. Conclude that the story is describing bricks. Then have students share their answers about why bricks are still used today. The General Shale Museum of Ancient Brick in Tennessee is the museum to which the story refers. Malvern, Arkansas is considered the "Brick Capital of the World" because of its massive yearly production of bricks. Ask students to hypothesize why this city became a producer of bricks. Conclude that its location near clay deposits made it a suitable site for brick production.

2. Have students circle and write two sets of story synonyms (famous/notable, old/ancient). Then have students circle and write *built, almost, hot, several.* Ask students to substitute a synonym for these words in the story so that the meaning is not changed.

3. Write the words *build, gone, stand, dried,* and *stories* on the chalkboard. Then have students write these words. Next to each, have them write another word form for the word used in the story (built, goes, stood, dry, story). Have students check their spellings against the story words.

4. Have students circle and write the story words *on, first, dry, later, now, hot, answer.* Then have them write an antonym for each.

DICTATION REVIEW 75

Materials: pencil, writing paper

Core Words

state	371	stood	373	ten	375
list	372	hundred	374		

Review Core Words

the (1), of (2), a (4), to (5), in (6), you (8), that (9), with (17), be (21), have (25), one (28), can (38), your (40), which (41), if (44), would (59), more (63), than (73), people (79), why (136), every (151), name (155), want (193), live (217), city(ies) (273), close (328), letter (344), person (367)

Extra Words

begins, middle, thousand, reasons

Have students write the sentences as they are dictated.

1. Can you list every state that begins with the letter M?
2. If you stood in the middle of your state, which city would be close to you?
3. Which cities in your state have more than one hundred thousand people?
4. Name ten reasons why a person would want to live in your state.

■ Follow-Up Activity

Have students answer the sentence questions and share their responses. If a state has no cities with a population of one hundred thousand, ask students to find out the population of the largest city.

REVIEW 76 Core Words 376–380
Use after Core Word 380

CLOZE STORY REVIEW 76

Materials: Master 76, pencil, writing paper

Core Words

fast	376	kept	378	can't	380
felt	377	notice	379		

Review Words

there (37), their (42), only (85), right (116), began (215), it's (253), young (256), really (313), ready (357), special (361), hundred (374)

Tell students that this story tells about a sport you can do at any age. Read the story as students write the words. Then have students research the information requested in the story and write what they learned.

Run for Fun

You (1) can't help but (2) notice that the sport of running has become popular. Some runners have (3) special gear for (4) their sport. (5) There must be a (6) hundred different running shoes claiming to make you go (7) fast! The (8) right shoes are important, but (9) it's training that (10) really counts. Wesley Paul (11) began running when he was (12) young. He (13) felt good about running and (14) kept training every day. He was (15) ready for a marathon when he was (16) only eight. What is a marathon and what can you learn about people who run in them?

■ Extend Learning

1. Have students share their answers to the story questions. Conclude that a marathon is a race 26 miles, 385 yards long. A Greek soldier ran from Athens to Marathon to bring news of his army's victory. A marathon is the same distance that soldier ran. Students can find information in periodicals and books about marathoners, such as the book *Wesley Paul, Marathon Runner* by Julianna A. Fogel.

2. Have students predict the spellings through the word preview procedure of the review story words *different, important, about, every, learn* and the new story words *sport, shoes, eight, running.* Have students check their predictions against the spelling of the story words.

3. Have students circle the four instances of the story word *running* and write the word. Discuss the base word *run* and the rule that applies for adding the *ing* suffix. Then have students find and write more words that follow this rule. Choices may include *get, top, ship, shop, step, trip, sit.* Then show how the past tense of *run* changes its spelling to *ran.* Have students find and write more words that follow this pattern. Choices may include *build/built, say/said, go/gone, find/found, give/gave.*

4. Have students circle and write the story word homophones. Choices may include *you, some, their, there, be, right, it's, for, eight, in.* Then have students write their homophone partners.

DICTATION REVIEW 76

Materials: pencil, writing paper

Core Words

fast	376	kept	378	can't	380
felt	377	notice	379		

Review Core Words

the (1), a (4), to (5), that (9), at (20), I (24), had (29), but (31), what (32), how (49), she (54), so (57), has (62), time(s) (69), my (80), just (97), know (100), good (106), me (110), too (112), even (130), food (198), mother (226), it's (253), told (255), thing (258), didn't (281), eat(ing) (303), table (314), remember (315), before (332), hundred (374)

Extra Words

hungry, ate, bad, manners

Have students write the sentences as they are dictated.

1. I felt so hungry that I ate my food too fast.
2. I can't even remember what I had, but I know I just kept eating.
3. It's a good thing that my mother didn't notice my bad manners.
4. She has told me a hundred times before how to eat at the table.

■ Follow-Up Activity

Have students write what this mother may have said and done if she noticed this "speedy eater" downing food. Prior to the writing, review use of punctuation for dialogue.

REVIEW 77 Core Words 381–385

Use after Core Word 385

CLOZE STORY REVIEW 77

Materials: Master 77, pencil, writing paper

Core Words

strong	381	probably	383	horse	385
voice	382	area	384		

Review Core Words

its (76), around (120), between (154), always (183), don't (190), better (245), it's (253), English (350), perhaps (352), complete (365), hundred (374)

Tell students that this is a riddle story. Read the story as students write the words. Then have students write answers for the two story riddles.

Riddle Time

"What (1) <u>always</u> sleeps with (2) <u>its</u> shoes on? A (3) <u>horse</u>!" If you (4) <u>voice</u> disapproval of this riddle's answer, (5) <u>it's</u> (6) <u>probably</u> because you know that all horses (7) <u>don't</u> have horseshoes. (8) <u>Perhaps</u> you'll like this one (9) <u>better</u>. "What runs (10) <u>around</u> an (11) <u>area</u> of the yard, but never moves? A fence!" Now here are two riddles for you to (12) <u>complete</u>. "What is the difference (13) <u>between</u> a storm cloud and a (14) <u>strong</u> lion with a toothache?" "What is the first thing that happens when one (15) <u>hundred</u> (16) <u>English</u> sheep dogs fall into Lake Erie?"

■ Extend Learning

1. Have students share their answers to the story riddles. Then share these answers with them: "What is the difference between a storm cloud and a strong lion with a toothache?" One pours with rain and the other roars with pain! "What is the first thing that happens when one hundred English sheep dogs fall into Lake Erie?" They get wet! Have students find and write favorite riddles. Compile them into a class book that provides the riddle answers in the back.

2. Have students circle and write the story words *because* and *between.* Then have them write more *be___* words. Choices may include *behind, before, believe, beyond, beside, begin, began, become, became.*

3. Have students circle and write the story words *its* and *it's.* Have them explain in writing how to know when to use each. Then have students write two sentences that use the homophones, leaving blanks for the words. Students can exchange sentences with a partner and fill in the appropriate missing homophones.

4. Have students write the story words *English sheep dogs.* Then have them work in pairs to write the names of more kinds of dogs, such as a *German shepherd.* Encourage the use of a dictionary to check spellings. Ask students to explain in writing why or why not the answer to the riddle would

change if another kind of dog was substituted for the English sheep dogs in the riddle.

DICTATION REVIEW 77

Materials: pencil, writing paper

Core Words

strong	381	probably	383	horse	385
voice	382	area	384		

Review Core Words

the (1), and (3), a (4), to (5), in (6), that (9),
it (10), was (13), would (59), more (63),
her (64), than (73), first (74), its (76), now (78),
may (89), called (96), get(ting) (101), right (116),
place (131), name (155), end (170), thought (179),
show (184), important (195), hear (260),
close (328), nothing (329), ready (357),
stood (373), probably (383), area (384)

Extra Words

evening, everyone, win, waiting

Have students write the sentences as they are dictated.

1. It was evening and the horse show was close to its end.
2. Everyone thought that May and her horse would probably win.
3. May stood ready in the area waiting to hear her name called in a strong voice.
4. Nothing was more important to May right now than getting first place.

■ Follow-Up Activity

Have students generalize about May and other winners of competitions that require a special skill. What character traits might these achievers have in common?

REVIEW 78 · Core Words 386–390

Use after Core Word 390

CLOZE STORY REVIEW 78

Materials: Master 78, pencil, writing paper

Core Words

matter	386	box	388	that's	390
stand	387	start	389		

Review Words

there (37), their (42), other(s) (60), until (196),
without (204), almost (216), because (334),
among (345), person (367), hold (370),
probably (383)

Tell students that this story is about a favorite movie-time snack. Read the story as students write the words. Then have students write the step-by-step directions for making popcorn.

Let's Have Popcorn

(1) <u>Hold</u> everything! Don't (2) <u>start</u> the movie (3) <u>until</u> I get my popcorn! A (4) <u>box</u> or dish of popcorn is (5) <u>almost</u> a necessity for movie watchers. People (6) <u>stand</u> in line to get (7) <u>their</u> popcorn at every theater. As a (8) <u>matter</u> of fact, popcorn is (9) <u>among</u> the most nutritious snacks if it's popped (10) <u>without</u> oil. (11) <u>That's</u> good news (12) <u>because</u> we consume a lot of popcorn. Now (13) <u>there</u> are special flavored popcorns. You've (14) <u>probably</u> made popcorn for yourself or (15) <u>others</u>. Write each step in the directions for a (16) <u>person</u> who has never made this snack.

■ Extend Learning

1. Have students share their directions for making popcorn. Have students critique the directions to determine if every step is stated.
2. Have students circle and write the four story word contractions (don't, it's, that's, you've). Then have students write the words that comprise these contractions.
3. Have students predict the spellings through the word preview procedure of the review story words *every, don't, people, most, it's, special, write* and the new story words *a lot, movie, popcorn, everything*. Have students check their predictions against the spelling of the story words.
4. Have students circle and write the story word compounds *everything, popcorn, yourself*. Then see how many more compound words they can write in three minutes. Award one point for each correctly spelled compound.

DICTATION REVIEW 78

Materials: pencil, writing paper

Core Words

83

Review Core Words

the (1), of (2), and (3), a (4), to (5), it (10), was (13), they (19), one (28), had (29), an (39), their (42), how (49), up (50), some (56), would (59), into (61), time (69), make(ing) (72), now (78), made (81), just (97), great (146), set (162), something (178), large (185), children (200), side (203), across (247), turned (270), money (279), idea (331), before (332)

Extra Words

bright, apple(s), sign, free

Have students write the sentences as they are dictated.

1. The children had the bright idea to set up an apple stand.
2. They made their sign across one side of a large box.
3. Now it was just a matter of time before they would start making money.
4. That's how they turned their free time and some apples into something great.

■ Follow-Up Activity

Have students create a fictitious flier advertising the availability of apples at the children's apple stand, including all the necessary information a buyer would want.

REVIEW 79 — Core Words 391–395

Use after Core Word 395

CLOZE STORY REVIEW

Materials: Master 79, pencil, writing paper

Core Words

class	391	surface	393	common	395
piece	392	river	394		

Review Words

there (37), their (42), both (180), children (200), live (217), across (247), sure (251), answer (265), though (330), hundred (374), that's (390)

Tell students that for this story they will need to wear their "thinking cap." Read the story as students write the words. Then have students work in cooperative groups to think through the dilemma the story poses.

Crossing the Water

Get a (1) <u>piece</u> of paper and a pencil. Start thinking. A boy in your (2) <u>class</u> has a problem. He, his brother, and two sisters (3) <u>live</u> on one side of the (4) <u>river</u>. The school is (5) <u>across</u> the water. (6) <u>Their</u> boat is a (7) <u>common</u> rowboat that can't hold more than a (8) <u>hundred</u> pounds or it's (9) <u>sure</u> to sink. The boys (10) <u>both</u> weigh 100 pounds and the girls weigh 50 pounds each. How can the boat be used to transport the (11) <u>children</u> safely? On the (12) <u>surface</u>, it seems as (13) <u>though</u> (14) <u>there</u> isn't a solution to this, but (15) <u>that's</u> not so. Yes, there's an (16) <u>answer</u>!

■ Extend Learning

1. Ask each group to explain how they tried to solve the problem. Then visually explain the solution using props. The two sisters get into the boat and row across the river. One sister goes ashore and waits while the other one rows back across the river. When she gets to the other side, she gets out of the boat and one of her brothers rows to the other side. This brother goes ashore and the waiting sister gets into the boat again and rows back across by herself. Then the two girls row together to the other side. When they get there, one of them gets out and the other one rows back across again. She gets out and her other brother rows across alone. Next, the sister waiting on the shore rows to the other side, gets her sister, and together they row across. They pull the boat ashore and head for school. Discuss the solution and repeat the explanation. Then have students demonstrate the solution together in their group. Interested students can pose this problem and demonstrate its solution to friends and family.

2. Have students circle and write the five story word contractions (can't, it's, isn't, that's, there's). Then have students write the homophones for the contractions *it's* and *there's* (its, theirs) and write these homophones in sentences.

3. On the chalkboard, write the words *finish, girl, less, adults, no, question.* Have students circle and write their story word antonyms.

DICTATION REVIEW 79

Materials: pencil, writing paper

Core Words

class	391	surface	393	common	395
piece	392	river	394		

Review Core Words

the (1), of (2), and (3), a (4), in (6), is (7), you (8), that (9), are (15), what (32), can (38), an (39), your (40), about (48), how (49), like (66), very (93), our (109), same (115), different (139), something (178), show (184), often (186), school (194), children (200), thing(s) (258), sea (267), body (285), fish (299)

Extra Words

share, lake, alike, apple

Have students write the sentences as they are dictated.

1. Very different things often share something in common.
2. Can you show how a river, a sea, and a lake are alike?
3. What is the same about the surface of our body and that of a fish?
4. How is a piece of an apple like a class of children in your school?

■ Follow-Up Activity

Have students write answers to the sentence questions. Then provide time to share the answers.

REVIEW 80 Core Words 396–400

Use after Core Word 400

CLOZE STORY REVIEW 80

Materials: Master 80, pencil, writing paper

Core Words

stop	396	talk	398	fine	400
am	397	whether	399		

Review Words

through (102), usually (278), family (287), really (313), idea(s) (331), shown (348), strong (381), probably (383), class (391), piece (392), common (395)

Tell students that this story will get them started making a new class book. Read the story as students write the words. Then have students research and write home remedies for a class book.

Home Remedies

How (1) <u>am</u> I going to (2) <u>stop</u> my hiccups? Eat a sugar cube. I can't get rid of my sore throat. Drink (3) <u>strong</u> tea with a (4) <u>piece</u> of lemon and some honey. (5) <u>Whether</u> or not these "cures" (6) <u>really</u> work depends upon to whom you (7) <u>talk</u>. Some home remedies (8) <u>probably</u> work (9) <u>fine</u> for (10) <u>common</u> problems, but for serious illnesses, a doctor (11) <u>usually</u> gives the best advice. Survey your friends and (12) <u>family</u> for home remedies that have (13) <u>shown</u> good results (14) <u>through</u> the years. Compile these get-well (15) <u>ideas</u> into a (16) <u>class</u> book.

■ Extend Learning

1. Have students share their home remedies and compile them into a class book.
2. Have students circle and write the story word homophones. Choices may include *sore, piece, some, whether, not, some, for, to, shown, through.* Then have students write their homophone partners. Discuss the homophones. Have students use selected homophones in written sentences.
3. Have students circle and write the story words *remedies* and *family.* Then have students write *remedy* and *families* and explain the *consonant-y* rule for making plurals that applies to these words. Compare this to *vowel-y* ending words. Have students circle and write the story word *survey* and make it plural.
4. Have students circle and write the story words *stop, get, drink, talk, work, give, survey, compile.* Then have them add the *ing* suffix to each. Discuss the spelling rules that apply.

DICTATION REVIEW 80

Materials: pencil, writing paper

Core Words

stop	396	talk	398	fine	400
am	397	whether	399		

Review Core Words

a (4), to (5), in (6), that (9), as (16), be(ing) (21),
from (23), I (24), have (25), or (26), not (30),
can (38), other(s) (60), who (77), people (79),
my (80), long (91), me (110), think(ing) (118),
around (120), say(ing) (149), being (233),
it's (253), heard (262), usually (278), I'm (284),
nothing (329), feel (355), special (361),
person (367), anything (369), voice (382)

Extra Words

worth, conversation, pretty, enjoy

Have students write the sentences as they are dictated.

1. I talk to people whether or not I have anything
   worth saying.
2. I feel fine as long as it's my voice being heard in
   a conversation.
3. Nothing can stop me from thinking that I'm
   pretty special.
4. Am I a person whom others usually enjoy
   being around?

■ Follow-Up Activity

Have students write an answer to the question posed.
Then have students think about this person and
speculate in writing why the person always wants
to be the center of attention. Is this person really
more important than anyone else?

REVIEW 1

Friends

Friends are nice **1** _____ each other. They

help each other. George **2** _____ Martha are

two hippo friends. George was hungry. Martha fixed George

3 _____ bowl **4** _____ soup.

But George didn't like **5** _____ soup.

If you were George, what would you do?

REVIEW 2

Name _____

A Good Pet

This 1 _____ an animal 2 _____

makes a good pet. 3 _____ might give this animal

a dish 4 _____ milk. This animal looks for mice.

This animal may climb the fence 5 _____ walk

along 6 _____ . This animal may live

7 _____ your house or live outside. This animal

purrs. What could this be?

REVIEW 3

Name _____

Caps

There 1 _____ a man who had many caps

2 _____ sale. All these caps were

3 _____ his head. But no one wanted to buy any

4 _____ his caps. "These 5 _____

fine caps! I must sell them," said the man. 6 _____

needs help. Do you have an idea or two 7 _____

could help him?

REVIEW 4

Name _____

A Dandy Dandelion

Jennifer Giraffe invited Dandelion the Lion 1 _____

a party. He fixed 2 _____ hair and put

3 _____ new clothes. Dandelion looked

4 _____ if he could be in movies! Dandelion took

flowers 5 _____ him. 6 _____

were for Jennifer. But when he was 7 _____ her

door, she didn't know him. Why?

REVIEW 5

Name _____

A Number Game

Mine is red. The two **1** _____ yours look

blue. The boys **2** _____ four green ones.

3 _____ orange and yellow one is Kay's. She got it

4 _____ Mike. How many **5** _____

there in all? **6** _____ would like to know.

7 _____ sure that you count carefully.

REVIEW 6

Name _____

The Largest Land Animals

Which land animal is today's biggest? You may have

1 _____ the chance to see these big animals in a

zoo 2 _____ animal park. You might have seen

3 _____ go 4 _____ in a parade.

5 _____ have large ears 6 _____

a small tail. These huge animals do 7 _____ make

good house pets.

REVIEW 7

Name _____

Peter's Fun

Peter has a new baby sister. Now 1 _____ he

plays, he has to be quiet. He cannot be noisy. 2 _____

day he made two tall buildings 3 _____ his

blocks, 4 _____ they 5 _____

came crashing down! Mother told Peter that the blocks

6 _____ noisy. 7 _____ might

Peter do for quiet fun?

REVIEW

Name _____

The Weather

The sun may be shining as **1** _____ go to school.

Then **2** _____ school is out, **3** _____

are big rain clouds! You needed **4** _____ umbrella

after all! The weather **5** _____ fool us. Now

it's **6** _____ turn to predict our weather.

7 _____ will the weather be like tomorrow at

two o'clock?

REVIEW **9**

Name _____

The Race

1 _____ is an old story about a race between a

hare and a tortoise. The hare 2 _____ that he

would win! To begin, the two animals put 3 _____

toes at the starting line. Then they 4 _____ off!

5 _____ animal 6 _____ you

think won? 7 _____ you know this tale, you know

its surprise ending.

Core Words 41–45 ©1996 Rebecca Sitton's Spelling Sourcebook Reviews

REVIEW 10

Name _____

Date _____

Make a Bookmark

I 1 _____ tell you 2 _____ to

make a beautiful bookmark. 3 _____ of you needs

paper, scissors, 4 _____ crayons. Cut the paper to

5 _____ the size you want the bookmark. Write

6 _____ name 7 _____ at the top of

the paper. Then decorate 8 _____ paper by drawing

pretty goldfish or seashells. Now you 9 _____ a fine

bookmark! 10 _____ can you do with your bookmark?

The Little Red Hen Makes Bread

Once 1 _____ was a hen called the Little Red

Hen. 2 _____ wanted to make bread. This hen had

3 _____ friends. The hen asked 4 _____

for 5 _____ help. They all 6 _____

that they 7 _____ busy. So the hen made two loaves

of bread herself. 8 _____ the hot loaves came

9 _____ of the oven, they smelled so good!

10 _____ what do you think happened next?

REVIEW 12

Bears

1 _____ are 2 _____ animals that

sleep all winter. They hibernate. Bears hibernate in 3 _____

dens. 4 _____ in the spring they wake up

5 _____ that they can play and eat. They like to see

each 6 _____ . 7 _____ the

bears leave the dens, they are hungry. What do you think

8 _____ bears 9 _____ like to eat?

Do you 10 _____ an idea?

REVIEW 13

Name _____

Date _____

Happy Mice

I'd like you 1 _____ meet 2 _____

mice. 3 _____ lives are quite different. One lives

happily in 4 _____ country cottage. " 5 _____

is 6 _____ fresh air in the country," she

7 _____ . The other mouse lives well in the busy city.

"Come 8 _____ the city. You will like the

9 _____ things to see and do," the city mouse replied.

Which mouse do you think 10 _____ the best life? Why?

REVIEW 14

Name _____

Date _____

Friends and Letters

Do you have a friend 1 _____ you do not

2 _____ often? Perhaps you 3 _____

write to her or 4 _____ . It 5 _____

take only a short while to write this letter. It should take only a

minute for 6 _____ friend to read the letter. Letters

7 _____ a good way to make our friendships last for a

long, long 8 _____ . Who might 9 _____

to get a friendly letter 10 _____ you?

REVIEW 15

Name _____

Date _____

The Loose Tooth

1 _____ one tooth fell out and then another! All the

students 2 _____ losing 3 _____ baby

teeth 4 _____ Arthur. Arthur had 5 _____

wiggling his loose tooth for a long time. More 6 _____

anything, Arthur wished he 7 _____ get this tooth

out. But 8 _____ amount of wiggling seemed to

9 _____ it come loose. Is 10 _____

help for poor Arthur? How might he get his tooth out?

Core Words 71–75 ©1996 Rebecca Sitton's Spelling Sourcebook Reviews

REVIEW 16

Name _____

Date _____

Straw Painting

Many 1 _____ 2 _____ have never

painted before are straw painting 3 _____ . Two of

4 _____ friends tried it. 5 _____

they put some paint drops on paper. 6 _____ they blew

through one end of a straw. Air came out 7 _____

other end. The air blew the paint drops here and 8 _____

to make 9 _____ picture. "Wow! It's more fun

10 _____ brush painting!" they all said.

REVIEW 17

Name _____

Date _____

Make a Wish

Day was almost 1 _____ . Soon the night sky

2 _____ be full of 3 _____

bright stars shining 4 _____ on me. Now I

5 _____ see 6 _____ one star.

It was the first star. 7 _____ twinkle was brighter

8 _____ any star I had ever seen. I fixed my eyes

upon it and I 9 _____ a wish. Have you ever

wished upon a star? 10 _____ your wish come true?

Core Words 81–85 ©1996 Rebecca Sitton's Spelling Sourcebook Reviews

REVIEW 18

1 _____

You can 2 _____ this up in a cloud or see it in the

sea. It can 3 _____ power for our electric lights.

4 _____ might 5 _____ it when they are thirsty

or when they clean 6 _____ dog. It 7 _____

disappear if you heat it, 8 _____ if you freeze it, it takes up

9 _____ space. Sometimes 10 _____

is too much or too little of it. Either 11 _____ , it's a

problem for us. 12 _____ name begins with w.

REVIEW **19**

Name _____

Date _____

Name Game

Here's a game for you. Write your **1** _____ name in

2 _____ big capital letters **3** _____

the side of your paper. **4** _____ every letter, write two

5 _____ that tell something **6** _____ you.

7 _____ one must begin **8** _____ that letter

of your name. If you have a **9** _____ name, you must think

of **10** _____ ways to describe yourself. **11** _____

with short names will have a **12** _____ less to do.

Core Words 91–95 ©1996 Rebecca Sitton's Spelling Sourcebook Reviews

Name _____

Date _____

Puzzle Fun

First, find a place to work 1 _____ you can cut and paste.

Choose the picture you like 2 _____ of all 3 _____ an

old magazine. Cut 4 _____ the picture. 5 _____

paste it on heavy paper that is a 6 _____ larger

7 _____ the picture. 8 _____ the

paste dries, cut the picture into pieces. Do you 9 _____

what you 10 _____ made? It's 11 _____

a puzzle! Can you put 12 _____ puzzle together?

Core Words 96–100 ©1996 Rebecca Sitton's Spelling Sourcebook Reviews

REVIEW 21

The Sky is Falling

Once a small acorn fell 1 _____ an oak tree. It came down

2 _____ the air and hit Chicken 3 _____

on the 4 _____ of her head. 5 _____

this chicken did not always use very 6 _____ good sense.

She 7 _____ to her friends, "The sky is falling! It struck

me! 8 _____ help! 9 _____ tell the king!"

If it had 10 _____ you on 11 _____

this tiny acorn fell, what would you 12 _____ done?

Core Words 101–105 ©1996 Rebecca Sitton's Spelling Sourcebook Reviews

REVIEW 22

Spelling Homophones

Help 1 _____ ! I'm a 2 _____ speller, except

for 3 _____ I 4 _____ homophones.

These 5 _____ sound alike, but 6 _____

have different letters and meanings. For example, if you're writing "in

an hour," *hour* isn't spelled 7 _____ " 8 _____

class." Or if you're writing "knew the answer," *knew* is not spelled the

same 9 _____ "a 10 _____ coat." Do

11 _____ ever learn to 12 _____ the right letters?

Core Words 106–110 ©1996 Rebecca Sitton's Spelling Sourcebook Reviews

REVIEW 23

More Than One

1 _____ spell the word 2 _____ means

more than one 3 _____ , you just 4 _____

an *s* at the end of the word. It works the 5 _____ way with

almost 6 _____ word. One dog is spelled *dog*, but

7 _____ of them becomes *dogs*. One book is *book*, but if you

8 _____ four of them it is *books*. Is this 9 _____

easy for you? Well 10 _____ , do you 11 _____

the spelling for *more than one* 12 _____ ?

REVIEW 24

Name _____

Date _____

The Parade is Coming!

They 1 _____ all sitting down along the edge

2 _____ the street waiting for the parade to come by.

" 3 _____ ! Listen!" called one of them. "I 4 _____

I hear it!" Soon 5 _____ was music all 6 _____

them 7 _____ the band came marching 8 _____ .

Can you see 9 _____ marchers? 10 _____

feet are stepping to the beat—left, 11 _____ , left.

Can you 12 _____ hear the big drums?

Core Words 116–120 ©1996 Rebecca Sitton's Spelling Sourcebook Reviews

Three Pigs and a Wolf

The 1 _____ pig did not 2 _____ long

to build his straw house. It would 3 _____ down with

a huff and a puff. 4 _____ was 5 _____

pig who used 6 _____ sticks to make his place. The third

pig took 7 _____ days to construct his home of strong bricks.

8 _____ along 9 _____ a hungry wolf. He

looked at the 10 _____ homes. 11 _____

do you suppose this wolf 12 _____ thinking?

REVIEW 26

Making Things to Make a Living

The family works 1 _____ the day and 2 _____

after dark 3 _____ they 4 _____ make

things for the market. They grow 5 _____ food.

The 6 _____ they don't eat goes to the market. They

7 _____ make new brooms, candles, and mittens

for 8 _____ . At the fall market, they sell or trade all

9 _____ good things to make 10 _____ living.

How 11 _____ 12 _____ family make a living?

REVIEW 27

Musical Glasses

You can make a musical instrument with things you find

1 _____ the house. It is 2 _____ an easy

thing to do. 3 _____ is how. 4 _____

5 _____ drinking glasses in a row and fill

6 _____ with a different amount of 7 _____ .

To play, you 8 _____ tap the glasses with a spoon. Add

9 _____ glasses for an 10 _____ better

sound. 11 _____ time to practice. Soon you will play

12 _____ .

Core Words 131–135 ©1996 Rebecca Sitton's Spelling Sourcebook Reviews

REVIEW 28

Name _____

Date _____

Finding Information in a Book

1 _____ is a way to easily 2 _____

information in a book. The table of contents lists the 3 _____

chapters. 4 _____ 5 _____ the big

dictionary 6 _____ the book's glossary tells the

meanings of important 7 _____ . The index can

8 _____ you, 9 _____ . It lists the pages

that tell 10 _____ a topic. 11 _____

do you 12 _____ the glossary and index are in

alphabetical order?

Name _____

Date _____

Using a Map

1 _____ we 2 _____ on a car trip, we

did not start 3 _____ without 4 _____ map.

5 _____ did we 6 _____ a map? A map

can be a big help! The map told us 7 _____ the mountains

and lakes were. It showed us the 8 _____ of miles between

cities. We looked at the map over and over 9 _____ . By the

10 _____ we got home, we had 11 _____

memories, but a map that looked 12 _____ !

Core Words 141–145 ©1996 Rebecca Sitton's Spelling Sourcebook Reviews

REVIEW 30

Name _____

Date _____

The Dentist

Doctor De Soto is a 1 _____ dentist known

2 _____ the world. All his patients 3 _____

that he is the best and 4 _____ about the times he fixed

5 _____ teeth. Now, 6 _____ dentists

are 7 _____ or women. But Doctor De Soto is

8 _____ . He is a 9 _____ mouse. What

10 _____ you 11 _____ to him if he

walked 12 _____ the door to help you as you sat

waiting in his dental chair?

Name _____

Date _____

It's Lost

Mother wrote May's 1 _____ on her lunch ticket

and gave it to her when she 2 _____ to school. But

3 _____ May got to school, 4 _____

was no ticket. She looked, but 5 _____ her ticket

was no 6 _____ to be 7 _____ .

8 _____ was it? Had she lost it 9 _____

home and school? 10 _____ now and

11 _____ , things get lost. 12 _____

you ever lost something important to you?

Core Words 151–155 ©1996 Rebecca Sitton's Spelling Sourcebook Reviews

REVIEW 32

Name _____

Date _____

Trucks

1 _____ are many 2 _____ kinds

of trucks. Some are 3 _____ and carry heavy loads,

4 _____ as large moving vans that transport furniture

to your new 5 _____ . Some are refrigerated to

6 _____ 7 _____ loads a cool ride. These

trucks may carry ice cream 8 _____ it 9 _____

not be in warm 10 _____ 11 _____

the dairy and the store. What other special trucks can you

12 _____ ?

REVIEW 33

Name _____

Date _____

Draw It

Get 1 _____ to learn to draw your 2 _____

pictures that look 3 _____ like the real thing! You can

4 _____ books for help. The authors are artists who share

5 _____ ideas and talents. 6 _____ show

how to make 7 _____ 8 _____ to create

flowers, a cat, or 9 _____ a dinosaur. In the library,

you can look for books listed 10 _____ "drawing."

11 _____ are many good ones to be 12 _____ .

REVIEW 34

Name _____

Date _____

Eponyms

You may not have heard of *eponyms,* 1 _____ you

2 _____ them. They 3 _____ words named

for a person or a 4 _____ . George Ferris invented

5 _____ Ferris wheel. We 6 _____ knew

him, but we 7 _____ his 8 _____ name.

In the 9 _____ , Mr. Ferris 10 _____ all

of 11 _____ with a carnival ride and an eponym. Can you

12 _____ the origins of *OK, Graham cracker, hamburger,*

jeans, or *guppy?*

REVIEW 35

Name _____

Date _____

The Lion and the Mouse

1 _____ the lion was asleep, a 2 _____

mouse ran 3 _____ his nose. This awoke the lion and

he seized the tiny mouse. Mouse was afraid 4 _____ he

thought the lion 5 _____ eat him. 6 _____ ,

in a squeaky 7 _____ the mouse pleaded, "Oh,

8 _____ lion, do not harm me for I promise to

9 _____ you one day." How do you 10 _____

a 11 _____ mouse 12 _____ aid this

big lion?

Core Words 171–175 ©1996 Rebecca Sitton's Spelling Sourcebook Reviews

REVIEW 36

Name _____

Date _____

The Golden Gate Bridge

Joseph Strauss built 1 _____ that people 2 _____

know and love today. In the 1920's, he 3 _____ the need

for a bridge 4 _____ San Francisco and the land north of

5 _____ . He 6 _____ it would help people

get to and 7 _____ the city, as well as add a fine structure to

the area. But 8 _____ then, others 9 _____

Strauss wasn't 10 _____ . 11 _____ , no one

12 _____ ever build a bridge across the water 13 _____ .

Second, such a bridge would 14 _____ look beautiful.

Core Words 176–180 ©1996 Rebecca Sitton's Spelling Sourcebook Reviews

REVIEW 37

Name _____

Date _____

The Disappearing Dinosaurs

I've 1 _____ wanted to know why all the 2 _____

dinosaurs disappeared 65 million years ago. No one can really

3 _____ me why for sure, but a 4 _____ people

have made very good guesses. Some think it was 5 _____ of

6 _____ much cold weather. Then 7 _____

are 8 _____ who say that 9 _____ food was

in short supply. I'd like to 10 _____ to find 11 _____

more theories 12 _____ our great vanishing dinosaurs. Where

13 _____ information like this be 14 _____ ?

REVIEW 38

Name _____

Date _____

Amelia Bedelia

Amelia Bedelia is a maid in Peggy Parish's books. She 1 _____

works for Mr. and Mrs. Rogers in 2 _____ big 3 _____ .

Once 4 _____ 5 _____ her to bake a sponge

cake. As Amelia put the ingredients 6 _____ , she added a large

kitchen sponge. Mrs. Rogers 7 _____ 8 _____ ,

"Now 9 _____ forget to dust the furniture and change the

towels in 10 _____ bathroom." So Amelia put dust all

11 _____ the furniture. 12 _____ do you

13 _____ Amelia did with 14 _____ towels?

REVIEW 39

Name _____

Date _____

Tick-Tock Clocks

What time is it? Have you 1 _____ that question yet today?

People 2 _____ 3 _____ to know the time. The

4 _____ seems to be run by clocks! Clocks 5 _____

us know when to leave for 6 _____ 7 _____

day. They tell us when we're 8 _____ to lunch and 9 _____

us the 10 _____ time to get ready for bed. Clocks are so

11 _____ that they are all 12 _____ us.

13 _____ is an alarm clock, a watch, and a grandfather clock.

Write the name of 14 _____ kind of clock.

Core Words 191–195 ©1996 Rebecca Sitton's Spelling Sourcebook Reviews

REVIEW 40

Perfectly Practiced

1 _____ 2 _____ will later become

3 _____ world athletes? These youngsters 4 _____

good sports habits at an early age. They 5 _____ practicing, they

eat healthy 6 _____ , and in 7 _____ heart they

8 _____ to be 9 _____ . Nadia Comaneci,

a Rumanian gymnast, was one of these kids. 10 _____ Nadia

11 _____ to the 1976 Olympics, no gymnast had scored a perfect ten!

She did it! Then she did it 12 _____ seven 13 _____

times! She will 14 _____ be remembered.

REVIEW 41

The Grand Canyon

The Grand Canyon is such a 1 _____ and beautiful

2 _____ of 3 _____ . 4 _____

one 5 _____ to the other, it measures up to 18 miles wide.

6 _____ steep cliffs plunge over 5,000 7 _____

deep. And 8 _____ a doubt, it's getting bigger every day! It is

the 9 _____ of over 67 kinds of mammals, 32 reptile species,

and 291 10 _____ birds. Many 11 _____

and girls live with 12 _____ families in or near the canyon,

13 _____ . How could such a grand canyon have been created?

Core Words 201–205 ©1996 Rebecca Sitton's Spelling Sourcebook Reviews

The Returning Cats

The Moore family had the surprise of their 1 _____ ! Tabby

Cat got lost on their vacation to Utah. Sadly, they 2 _____

for home 3 _____ her. 4 _____ they got

5 _____ to Idaho, they 6 _____ they'd get

7 _____ cat. Before they did, Tabby showed up! It 8 _____

the 9 _____ three months, but she did return! 10 _____

people have told similar stories for us to 11 _____ that this is

not unusual. But it is a big mystery how 12 _____ cats

13 _____ their way 14 _____ distances home.

REVIEW 43

Name _____

Date _____

Is it a Bug or an Insect?

We 1 _____ 2 _____ the nickname bugs for

all insects. A bug is really one 3 _____ of insect. All insects have

a 4 _____ , a thorax, and an abdomen. If the insect is a bug, it

5 _____ has 6 _____ wings. Fossils 7 _____

that insects have 8 _____ 9 _____ since life

10 _____ . Flying insects had the skies 11 _____

all to themselves long before pterodactyls, birds, or bats 12 _____

to the 13 _____ . Some 14 _____ big. Ancient

dragonflies had wings twenty-nine inches wide!

REVIEW 44

Name _____

Date _____

How Important is Paper?

Could you 1 _____ 2 _____ paper? 3 _____

would surely change if you took all the paper 4 _____ this

5 _____ . Let's follow you 6 _____ a day.

7 _____ , you 8 _____ for the bathroom.

9 _____ is no toilet paper! Don't try to blow your nose either.

No tissue. You 10 _____ 11 _____ have breakfast

cereal, but it's not in a box. Find a new container for your sack lunch, too.

Where's the sports 12 _____ ? 13 _____ the

picture? Continue this, on 14 _____ sheet of . . . *paper.*

Core Words 216–220 ©1996 Rebecca Sitton's Spelling Sourcebook Reviews

Name _____

Date _____

You're in Business

Have you ever 1 _____ of starting an errand service after

2 _____ ? Busy people 3 _____ help. You

4 _____ give them a 5 _____ running errands

that 6 _____ take you 7 _____ from home. Charge

for your service, but not too 8 _____ a price. You want them to

call you 9 _____ . Your business will grow 10 _____

folks know 11 _____ can count on you. Before the school

12 _____ is over, you'll have more 13 _____

14 _____ business and a cookie jar full of cash!

Old Tale, New Ending

" 1 _____ upon a time, 2 _____ was a bear

family living happily in a 3 _____ cottage. One morning when

the 4_____ , the 5 _____ , and the baby bear

sat down to eat 6 _____ porridge, it was 7 _____

hot. So they turned off the 8 _____ and took a walk in the

woods to 9 _____ the 10 _____ cool." You

11 _____ what happened in this story 12 _____

the bears were away. However, this time 13 _____ else happened.

14 _____ what took place in a new version of the tale.

The Day With No Electricity

1 _____ this 2 _____ in your head. It is

3 _____ at your house. For the time 4 _____ ,

5 _____ everyone for miles 6 _____ is asleep.

But before the 7 _____ of a 8 _____ day begins,

all the electricity on 9 _____ goes 10 _____ !

What happens? First, if you have an electric alarm clock, you sleep on. But

the 11 _____ you do awake, 12 _____ is a

13 _____ of problems ahead for you and others. Describe the

difficulties that may arise on this "day 14 _____ electricity."

Core Words 231–235 ©1996 Rebecca Sitton's Spelling Sourcebook Reviews

REVIEW 48

Name _____

Date _____

The 1 _____ 2 _____

In the 3 _____ 1814, the British invaded America's capital

city. 4 _____ burned much of the President's mansion and

other 5 _____ government buildings. The American

6 _____ quickly 7 _____ to work 8 _____

making plans to rebuild. 9 _____ their city was like new. The

President's mansion sparkled with fresh paint. 10 _____

11 _____ then, this great mansion has 12 _____

known by a special name. 13 _____ this distinctive name

14 _____ for the 15 _____ title.

Core Words 236–240 ©1996 Rebecca Sitton's Spelling Sourcebook Reviews

REVIEW 49

Name _____

Date _____

How To Do It

Get 1 _____ and pencil. 2 _____ a dictionary

3 _____ you. 4 _____ write the directions for

how to do 5 _____ . You might find this 6 _____

7 _____ every step must be included. Each 8 _____

should say exactly 9 _____ you mean. When you are

10 _____ , reread the directions and rewrite the parts you

11 _____ you can make 12 _____ . Then ask

a friend to follow 13 _____ directions. This will tell you how

well the directions you wrote 14 _____ written.

REVIEW 50

Water Wings for Horses

The "spirit of invention" has changed the 1 _____ !

2 _____ , some inventions 3 _____

became popular. 4 _____ the era of horse travel, William Ernest

invented 5 _____ that he 6 _____ was the

7 _____ way to cross deep rivers. It was two 8 _____

big rubber bags that 9 _____ be filled with 10 _____

to attach to a horse's stomach. 11 _____ horse and rider would

float 12 _____ the river. 13 _____ do you

think this invention is not one we remember 14 _____ ?

REVIEW 51

Name _____

Date _____

Sing a Song

1 _____ is a song you 2 _____ when you

were little that you 3 _____ sing 4 _____ .

It is 5 _____ to be sung to you 6 _____

a year. We are 7 _____ that 8 _____ the

most 9 _____ sung song! Mildred Hill, a Kentucky

teacher, wrote the melody and her sister Patty Hill, a principal, wrote

10 _____ words. 11 _____ , long ago the

words 12 _____ , "Good morning to all, Good morning to

all." 13 _____ to sing this song with these words.

14 _____ write it the way all of us know it best.

To Fly Like a Hawk

1 _____ was only one 2 _____ that Rudy

wanted in the 3 _____ world. Ever 4 _____

he was a very 5 _____ child, he 6 _____

he wanted to fly. He did not 7 _____ himself flying like a

8 _____ sparrow, but soaring 9 _____ the

sky like a hawk! Up to the 10 _____ he would glide! He

would be able to 11 _____ the wind! However, everyone

12 _____ , "People 13 _____ fly." Yet,

Rudy had a wish. Have you a wish? Write about your wish and tell why it's

14 _____ to you.

REVIEW 53

Name _____

Date _____

Flip a Coin

1 _____ ancient times, people 2 _____

it was best to let the gods make 3 _____ big decisions

for them. The people 4 _____ ask the gods a question and

hope the gods 5 _____ it. Then they waited for an

6 _____ that 7 _____ come to them

in one of 8 _____ ways. For 9 _____ ,

people might 10 _____ pocket 11 _____ to

flip a coin. If it landed heads, that meant the gods 12 _____

"yes." Tails meant "no." We still flip a coin to decide 13 _____

things 14 _____ .

REVIEW 54

Name _____

Date _____

Sam's Stories

Sam, whose real 1 _____ was Samantha, lived with

her 2 _____ and her cat on a 3 _____

island surrounded by the 4 _____ . Perhaps

5 _____ she was alone 6 _____ of the

time, Sam created big stories. 7 _____ people

8 _____ them lies. As she sat in her 9 _____

on the 10 _____ floor of her house watching the waves hit

11 _____ the shore, her mind always 12 _____

to fancy tales. None 13 _____ true. 14 _____

tall tale might Sam be telling now?

Its Fleece Was White as Snow

All children 1 _____ about Mary's 2 _____

lamb that "made the 3 _____ laugh and 4 _____ ."

This rhyme was written in 1830 by Sarah Hale from the 5 _____

of Boston. The 6 _____ of her short poem was to tell

7 _____ a real happening in 8 _____ a

lamb following its 9 _____ owner 10 _____

a 11 _____ school. The first 12 _____

lines of the poem 13 _____ the first words

14 _____ recorded. Thomas Edison said the rhyme into

his invention, the phonograph.

Mystery Coins

Jason was proud of 1 _____ . Of course, part of his success

may be 2 _____ as good luck. 3 _____ , luck

4 _____ runs out after awhile and Jason was 5 _____

right on his first 6 _____ . This is the 7 _____ of

thing Jason could do. If you secretly wrote on a piece of 8 _____

an amount of 9 _____ and the 10 _____

of coins it took to total that amount, Jason could tell you the coins. For

11 _____ , you might say, "The amount I have is sixty cents.

12 _____ made up of 13 _____ coins." Jason

was 14 _____ to have the correct 15 _____ .

What would Jason have 16 _____ you?

REVIEW 57

Name _____

Date _____

How Do Advertisements Persuade?

" 1 _____ not going to buy a new automobile 2 _____

I don't need one." That's what the man 3 _____ before he

saw the 4 _____ advertised in the 5 _____

newspaper. He was 6 _____ when he said he

7 _____ *need* one, but the ad made him *want* one. The ad

showed the 8 _____ of the auto and gave 9 _____

reasons to buy it. 10 _____ the man 11 _____

this auto was the 12 _____ thing for 13 _____

and his family. The ad worked! An ad 14 _____ attempts to

persuade you to buy something. Find an ad. How 15 _____ it

16 _____ to persuade you to buy?

REVIEW 58

Name _____

Date _____

Catch Yourself a Pet

1 _____ kinds of 2 _____ make good

3 _____ pets. A frog is one. Try to catch a frog. Frogs are

4 _____ found 5 _____ a rock by a pond.

6 _____ hard to sneak up on a frog and catch it in your hands.

7 _____ frogs 8 _____ quickly. A net at the end of a

long pole may 9 _____ better. 10 _____ captured,

be gentle. 11 _____ your frog loose inside a big box. This

will be 12 _____ home. Be 13 _____ there's

14 _____ in a tray at the bottom. Feed your new pet flies, worms,

and spiders. 15 _____ , put your frog back where you caught

it. Then go catch 16 _____ one.

REVIEW 59

Name _____

Date _____

Fact or Opinion?

A fact is a statement that is 1 _____ true. On the other

2 _____ , an opinion is something that a person or a

3 _____ believes, but isn't necessarily true. For

4 _____ , "the 5 _____ of George Washington is on

the US dollar bill" is a fact. " 6 _____ is the 7 _____

color for the front 8 _____ to a 9_____ ," is

an opinion. Now it's your 10 _____ to decide which is which.

11 _____ , "it costs 12 _____ much to get your hair

13 _____ ." 14 _____ , "night occurs when day

is 15 _____ ." Why is it important to know the difference

16 _____ facts and opinions? Write your opinion.

REVIEW 60

Flags

Flags have been waving 1 _____ history 2 _____

ancient times. They fly high 3 _____ buildings, on top of

ships, and lead every parade 4 _____ ever was! Every

5 _____ and state creates 6 _____ own flag.

Almost 7 _____ of them use a 8 _____

9 _____ color in the design. Some 10 _____

the body or head of 11 _____ , birds, or 12 _____ .

Some show 13 _____ or trees, or 14 _____

leaves or fruit. 15 _____ feature the sun, moon, or stars.

How would a 16 _____ create a flag to represent them?

Divide into student sets of two or three and design your own flag.

REVIEW 61

Sailing Through Life with Flying Colors

Are you 1 _____ a colorful 2 _____ in the

3 _____ ? Do you live 4 _____ in the

Blue Mountains, the 5 _____ Hills, or on Grays Peak? Are you green

with envy when you 6 _____ they're painting the town red in the

7 _____ of Green Bay? Do you go 8 _____

water rafting 9 _____ the Red River or swim

10 _____ Red Lake? Do you 11 _____ the

yellow pages? Are you tickled pink to 12 _____ oranges

13 _____ school and have a "blue plate special" for dinner? Do

you read 14 _____ mysteries 15 _____

Encyclopedia Brown? Can you add more to this 16 _____ ?

Name _____

Date _____

A Buffalo Tale

Years ago, buffalo herds 1 _____ a source of 2 _____

for the Native American people 3 _____ on the Great

Plains. The tribes needed the buffalo in 4 _____ to live.

First, the buffalo 5 _____ the people 6 _____ .

Then the buffalo hide was used in many 7 _____ ways,

8 _____ as for robes and tepee covers. The people were

9 _____ about 10 _____ respect for the

beast. The native storytellers would never 11 _____ short of tales

12 _____ the glorious buffalo. One of 13 _____

stories is 14 _____ in the 15 _____

Buffalo Woman by Paul Goble. Can you 16 _____ others?

REVIEW 63

Name _____

Date _____

A Breakfast Treat

On a 1 _____ winter 2 _____ when the

3 _____ is covered with snow, it's 4 _____

a treat to have piping hot pancakes! Can you 5 _____ the smell

of the maple syrup at 6 _____ breakfast 7 _____ ?

Maple syrup comes from the sugar maple tree. Native Americans

8 _____ it "maple water" 9 _____ it

dripped from the bark as sap. 10 _____ were the

11 _____ to 12 _____ how to boil the sap

13 _____ it became sweet syrup. Now the production of the

syrup is a big industry for 14 _____ in 15 _____

parts of the 16 _____ , as well as in Canada.

Name _____

Date _____

A Favorite Holiday

1 _____ holiday is your favorite? Thanksgiving, the oldest

2 _____ holiday, is 3 _____ celebrated

around the dinner 4 _____ . Of 5 _____ ,

Independence Day is a 6 _____ day for 7 _____

picnics. You 8 _____ choose Christmas 9 _____

it's fun to decorate the 10 _____ and place it in

11 _____ of a window for all to see. If you observe Hanukkah,

you may 12 _____ to choose it. 13 _____

about Halloween with 14 _____ costumes that transform

people into such things as 15 _____ rangers and ghosts?

Or your 16 _____ birthday may be the best day of all!

REVIEW 65

Measure Your Thinking Ability

A long time 1 _____ , my mother gave me a book of riddles,

but the 2 _____ page was gone from 3 _____ of it.

4 _____ of the riddles were easy, however, 5 _____

was one that 6 _____ stumped me. 7 _____

one morning I read the riddle and 8 _____ about it

9 _____ the day. I was 10 _____ until I finally

solved the puzzle 11 _____ that night. Can you figure it out?

"What has a foot on 12 _____ side and one in the middle?"

13 _____ , some words have more 14 _____ one

meaning. That's the 15 _____ hint 16 _____

give you. Just keep trying 17 _____ you have it!

REVIEW 66

Name _____

Date _____

Crazy Cut-Out Characters

1 _____ I made a cut-out. First, I 2 _____

3 _____ all the things I'd need—a pencil, glue,

4 _____ , and scissors. First, I drew a big circle for a

5 _____ . I had old magazines 6 _____ by to

7 _____ for cut outs. Next, I cut out 8 _____

colored eyes, large ears, and a bright red mouth. I glued them on the circle

to make a funny 9 _____ . Even 10 _____

my cut-up person was looking very silly, I 11 _____ that

12 _____ was 13 _____ foolish. I glued

14 _____ legs and arms to a 15 _____ . Last, I put on two

fish for feet! Now it's your 16 _____ to make a very crazy cut-out!

REVIEW 67

Name _____

Date _____

A Contraption Becomes an Invention

1 _____ laughed at Kirkpatrick Macmillan's 2 _____ .

A silly contraption he was making 3 _____ the town joke.

Never 4 _____ had anyone 5 _____ anything

like it. It had two big wheels with a seat. Macmillan 6 _____

he planned to ride it. Even 7 _____ he fell or hit something

8 _____ time he tried to ride the thing, he 9 _____

give up. He 10 _____ that he had to 11 _____

a brake. When the wheels came 12 _____ , he made them

stronger. He 13 _____ a life 14 _____

trial and error 15 _____ his invention finally worked.

16 _____ do you suppose he invented?

REVIEW 68

Name _____

Date _____

Picture Language

If you wanted to 1 _____ a story for your friends and

2 _____ , but letters of the alphabet hadn't been invented,

how 3 _____ you do it? 4 _____ the story!

5 _____ , it's easy to 6 _____ frustrated

and 7 _____ angry as you 8 _____ to

create pictures that say what you 9 _____ mean. Long

10 _____ , written language was mainly pictures, but of

11 _____ it was far 12 _____ effective

13 _____ reading the message in 14 _____ .

Research *ancient picture languages*. Look up *pictograph* and *hieroglyphics*.

15 _____ write one thing you 16 _____ .

REVIEW 69

Name _____

Date _____

Kite Communication

Today, 1 _____ are 2 _____ ways

of communicating with someone from afar. You might write a

3 _____ , send a FAX, use a computer online system,

or call on a telephone. Long ago, kites sent messages. The way a kite flew

4 _____ the 5 _____ , the kite's color, and

6 _____ shape were 7 _____ the ways kites

communicated. 8 _____ , the way in 9 _____ kites

flew in 10 _____ of and 11 _____ each other

meant 12 _____ . 13 _____ , kite communication

had a 14 _____ problems that 15 _____

modern kites 16 _____ overcome. What difficulties are these?

REVIEW 70

Name _____

Date _____

Watch Out for Idioms!

Knowing 1 _____ words 2 _____ not guarantee

that you'll be 3 _____ to understand the language. This is

4 _____ people use *idioms*. Idioms are words that say one

thing, but 5 _____ something else. 6 _____

the many 7 _____ would be this 8 _____ :

"This TV series is a 9 _____ !" If this comment gives

you the 10 _____ that a poodle or other canine will be

11 _____ in this TV show, you're wrong! Think of an idiom.

Then, 12 _____ one 13 _____ to show what

14 _____ actually saying and 15 _____ to

show what it 16 _____ intended to say.

REVIEW 71

Name _____

Date _____

Scream for Ice Cream

1 _____ love ice cream! 2 _____ is more ice

cream eaten in the 3 _____ 4 _____

in any country in the 5 _____ of the world. A 6 _____

favorite is the ice cream sundae. 7 _____ historians

8 _____ that this dessert was named for Sunday, even

9 _____ the two words are spelled differently. After people

worked hard for 10 _____ days, 11 _____

the seventh day was for enjoying 12 _____ "sundae."

13 _____ the greatest invention to increase the popularity of

this 14 _____ treat was the ice cream cone. Explore the

15 _____ story 16 _____ this super discovery.

Core Words 351–355 ©1996 Rebecca Sitton's Spelling Sourcebook Reviews

REVIEW 72

Name _____

Date _____

Making a Tepee

The word tepee 1 _____ "for living in." The 2 _____

tepees were 3 _____ by Native Americans of the Great Plains.

To make one, tall trees were cut and stripped of 4 _____

5 _____ leaves and branches to 6 _____ poles.

Three large poles were put 7 _____ to 8 _____

a tripod. Next, 9 _____ hides were 10 _____

to be attached to the poles and fastened to the 11 _____ . A

smoke hole was made at the top for venting the inside 12 _____ .

A flap for the 13 _____ door 14 _____

faced east. 15 _____ , 16 _____ was a

good reason for doing this. Can you explain why?

REVIEW 73

Name _____

Date _____

What Time Is It?

In the 1 _____ days, the 2 _____ bell was

a 3 _____ signal to tell the time. 4 _____ hour

on the hour, a bell ringer 5 _____ up the bell tower to ring the

bell. At noon and midnight, it rang a 6 _____ twelve times.

7 _____ , the bells did 8 _____ for those

who lived far from the 9 _____ . Country people

10 _____ told time by the sun, but some people used candle clocks.

The candle had marks 11 _____ 12 _____ side.

A 13 _____ hour had passed when the 14 _____

burned from one mark to the 15 _____ . 16 _____ ,

these clocks had a few problems. Explain these limitations.

Safety in the Kitchen

Safety is 1 _____ . For example, you must 2 _____

to take 3 _____ care when you are in the kitchen preparing

food. Almost 4 _____ in this room can be dangerous if it is

not used correctly. Over 5 _____ the kitchen accidents occur

6 _____ of careless use of knives. Do you 7 _____

all 8 _____ pots with a pot holder? 9 _____

be 10 _____ pot handles are 11 _____ to

the back or side of the stove so 12 _____ handles cannot be

bumped by a 13 _____ walking by. 14 _____ ,

15 _____ are a lot more safety ideas! Make a

16 _____ kitchen safety list.

REVIEW 75

Name _____

Date _____

What Are They?

The Empire 1 _____ Building was 2 _____

with 3 _____ million of them. The 4 _____

Wall of China stretches fifteen 5 _____ miles and contains

6 _____ four million. Their 7 _____ of

famous uses 8 _____ on! The 9 _____ ones

were probably 10 _____ by ancient Egyptians from mud that

11 _____ in the sun 12 _____ it was dry.

13 _____ it was cut into blocks. Now they're made from mined

clay mixed with 14 _____ to make a goo that's shaped and baked in

hot ovens. A Johnson City, Tennessee museum displays 15 _____

notable old ones. Now 16 _____ the story title.

REVIEW 76

Name _____

Date _____

Run for Fun

You 1 _____ help but 2 _____ that the sport

of running has become popular. Some runners have 3 _____

gear for 4 _____ sport. 5 _____ must be a

6 _____ different running shoes claiming to make you go

7 _____ ! The 8 _____ shoes are important,

but 9 _____ training that 10 _____

counts. Wesley Paul 11 _____ running when he was

12 _____ . He 13 _____ good about running and

14 _____ training every day. He was 15 _____

for a marathon when he was 16 _____ eight. What is a

marathon and what can you learn about people who run in them?

REVIEW 77

Name _____

Date _____

Riddle Time

"What 1 _____ sleeps with 2 _____ shoes

on? A 3 _____ !" If you 4 _____ disapproval

of this riddle's answer, 5 _____ 6 _____

because you know that all horses 7 _____ have horseshoes.

8 _____ you'll like this one 9 _____ .

"What runs 10 _____ an 11 _____ of the

yard, but never moves? A fence!" Now here are two riddles for you to

12 _____ . "What is the difference 13 _____

a storm cloud and a 14 _____ lion with a toothache?"

"What is the first thing that happens when one 15 _____

16 _____ sheep dogs fall into Lake Erie?

REVIEW 78

Name _____

Date _____

Let's Have Popcorn

1 _____ everything! Don't 2 _____ the movie

3 _____ I get my popcorn! A 4 _____ or dish

of popcorn is 5 _____ a necessity for movie watchers. People

6 _____ in line to get 7 _____ popcorn at every

theater. As a 8 _____ of fact, popcorn is 9 _____

the most nutritious snacks if it's popped 10 _____ oil.

11 _____ good news 12 _____ we consume

a lot of popcorn. Now 13 _____ are special flavored

popcorns. You've 14 _____ made popcorn for yourself

or 15 _____ . Write each step in the directions for a

16 _____ who has never made this snack.

REVIEW 79

Crossing the Water

Get a 1 _____ of paper and a pencil. Start thinking. A

boy in your 2 _____ has a problem. He, his brother, and two

sisters 3 _____ on one side of the 4 _____ .

The school is 5 _____ the water. 6 _____

boat is a 7 _____ rowboat that can't hold more than a

8 _____ pounds or it's 9 _____ to sink. The boys

10 _____ weigh 100 pounds and the girls weigh 50 pounds

each. How can the boat be used to transport the 11 _____

safely? On the 12 _____ , it seems as 13 _____

14 _____ isn't a solution to this, but 15 _____

not so. Yes, there's an 16 _____ !

Home Remedies

How 1 _____ I going to 2 _____

my hiccups? Eat a sugar cube. I can't get rid of my sore throat. Drink

3 _____ tea with a 4 _____ of lemon and some

honey. 5 _____ or not these "cures" 6 _____

work depends upon to whom you 7 _____ . Some home

remedies 8 _____ work 9 _____ for

10 _____ problems, but for serious illnesses, a doctor

11 _____ gives the best advice. Survey your friends and

12 _____ for home remedies that have 13 _____

good results 14 _____ the years. Compile these get-well

15 _____ into a 16 _____ book.

Materials Description

Rebecca Sitton's SPELLING SOURCEBOOK™ Series

published by **Egger Publishing, Inc.**
P.O. Box 12248, Scottsdale, AZ 85267
888-WE-SPELL (888-937-7355) • *FAX 480-951-2276*
Find us on the web at **www.sittonspelling.com**
Contact Rebecca at 480-473-7277
e-mail: **rsitton@sittonspelling.com**

Teacher Resource Books

SPELLING SOURCEBOOK™ 1
NECESSARY FOR TEACHERS OF ALL GRADES
Your source for the "how-to" and "why" for developing, inservicing, teaching day-to-day, and assessing your own language-integrated, skill-based spelling curriculum founded on the best practices supported by current spelling research. Reference resources include 1200 high-use writing words, game activities, and blackline masters.

SPELLING SOURCEBOOK™ 2 (Words 1–400)
NECESSARY FOR TEACHERS OF GRADES 1–4
Your source for skill-based activity ideas to extend every high-use Core Word 1–400. Teachers choose the activities that best meet their students' needs and abilities.

SPELLING SOURCEBOOK™ 3 (Words 401–800)
NECESSARY FOR TEACHERS OF GRADES 5–6
Your source for skill-based activity ideas to extend every high-use Core Word 401–800. Teachers choose the activities that best meet their students' needs and abilities.

SPELLING SOURCEBOOK™ 4 (Words 801–1200)
NECESSARY FOR TEACHERS OF GRADES 7–8
Your source for skill-based activity ideas to extend every high-use Core Word 801–1200. Teachers choose the activities that best meet their students' needs and abilities.

SPELLING SOURCEBOOK™ REVIEWS (Words 1–400)
NECESSARY FOR TEACHERS OF GRADES 1–4
Correlated to SOURCEBOOK™ 2, this is your source for Blackline Master Cloze Activities and Dictation Sentences for practice and assessment of every set of five sequential high-use Core Words 1–400.

SPELLING SOURCEBOOK™ REVIEWS (Words 401–800)
NECESSARY FOR TEACHERS OF GRADES 5–6
Correlated to SOURCEBOOK™ 3, this is your source for Blackline Master Cloze Activities and Dictation Sentences for practice and assessment of every set of five sequential high-use Core Words 401–800.

SPELLING SOURCEBOOK™ REVIEWS (Words 801–1200)
NECESSARY FOR TEACHERS OF GRADES 7–8
Correlated to SOURCEBOOK™ 4, this is your source for Blackline Master Cloze Activities and Dictation Sentences for practice and assessment of every set of five sequential high-use Core Words 801–1200.

WORD-WISE SOURCEBOOK™ Level 1
SUGGESTED FOR TEACHERS OF GRADES 1–2
Your source for the best of Dr. Barbara Schmidt's and Dr. Maurice Poe's laugh-aloud rhymes for learning spelling and language skills. Blackline master poems and activities feature Wordy Birdy.

WORD-WISE SOURCEBOOK™ Level 2
SUGGESTED FOR TEACHERS OF GRADES 3–4
Your source for the best of Dr. Barbara Schmidt's and Dr. Maurice Poe's laugh-aloud rhymes for learning spelling and language skills. Blackline master poems and activities feature Willy Wordster.

WORD-WISE SOURCEBOOK™ Level 3
SUGGESTED FOR TEACHERS OF GRADES 5–6
Your source for the best of Dr. Barbara Schmidt's and Dr. Maurice Poe's laugh-aloud rhymes for learning spelling and language skills. Blackline master poems and activities feature Inspector Clue-So.

SEMINAR HANDBOOK *Increasing Student Spelling Achievement*
Your source for follow-along use during and after live training seminars. Contains over 100 pages of reference information.

Teaching Aids

MY SPELL CHECK™ K–2 (pkg. of 10)
SUGGESTED FOR STUDENTS IN GRADES K–2
Your students' source for an alphabetical listing of 85 high-use writing words, with sections for animals, numbers, family, clothes, school, days, months, foods, and weather. Each card is 8½" x 11", in color on both sides. Package includes a teacher resource of over 50 word activities to extend the word bank. Packaged in sets of 10 cards with activities sheet.

SPELL CHECK™ 3–8 (pkg. of 10)
SUGGESTED FOR STUDENTS IN GRADES 3–8
Your students' source for an alphabetical listing of 150 high-use writing words, with references for months, days of the week, common abbreviations and 75 context sentences for often-confused words. Each card is 8½" x 11", in color on both sides. Package includes a teacher resource of over 50 word activities to extend the high-use word bank. Packaged in sets of 10 cards with activities sheet.

SPELLING WALL CHARTS (set of 5)
SUGGESTED FOR TEACHERS OF ALL GRADES
Your classroom source for five colorful charts: An alphabetical list of the 100 high-use writing words, context sentences for the *there* homophones, context sentences for the *to* homophones, a prefix poem, and the independent word-study procedure. Each package contains one each of the five different 18" x 24" wall charts.

Training Videos

STAFF DEVELOPMENT VIDEO SERIES
INCLUDES: VIDEO TAPE I   INTRODUCTION TO TEACHERS
VIDEO TAPE II   GRADING AND MANAGEMENT OPTIONS
VIDEO TAPE III INTRODUCTION TO PARENTS
TRAINING GUIDE FOR STAFF DEVELOPMENT
Recommended for all teachers using the SPELLING SOURCEBOOK™ Series.
Video Tape I (85 min.)   An essential introduction to the methodology and recommended follow-up to the training seminar. Rebecca explains exactly how to get started and guides teachers through one complete instructional unit.
Video Tape II (92 min.)   Rebecca contrasts Core Words and Priority Words, suggests Priority Word expectations, shows how to grade using six specific options, and provides extensive classroom management ideas.
Video Tape III (37 min.)   Assures parental and community support. Rebecca explains why changes in spelling instruction are necessary and how the SOURCEBOOK™ methods ensure spelling success for their children exactly where it counts—in everyday writing. Twelve parent-child spelling partnership activities are suggested.
Training Guide   For use with Video Tapes I and II to personalize and extend video training sessions. Includes step-by-step suggestions for the facilitator, discussion-promoting questions, activity-oriented ideas, and blackline masters for making the follow-along handbook for teacher participants.

PLEASE CALL FOR DUPLICATION/BROADCAST CONTRACT INFORMATION.

STAFF DEVELOPMENT SEMINARS
For a fast-paced "how-to" seminar conducted by Rebecca Sitton or one of her associates at your school site, call Egger Publishing, Inc.

FREE Information Package and (on-loan) Preview Video! Call toll free 888-WE-SPELL

Order Form

ORDER ANY 50 BOOKS FOR THE QUANTITY PRICE.

Rebecca Sitton's SPELLING SOURCEBOOK™ *Series*
published by **Egger Publishing, Inc.**
P.O. Box 12248, Scottsdale, AZ 85267
888-WE-SPELL (888-937-7355) • *FAX 480-951-2276*

	PRICE	QTY. PRICE	QTY.	TOTAL
GRADE 1				
Spelling SOURCEBOOK™ 1	$ 29.50	$ 24.50	_____	_____
The "How & Why" Book				
Spelling SOURCEBOOK™ 2	$ 29.50	$ 24.50	_____	_____
Activity Ideas for Words 1–400				
Spelling SOURCEBOOK™ Reviews	$ 39.50	$ 34.50	_____	_____
Assessments for Words 1–400				
GRADE 2				
Spelling SOURCEBOOK™ 1	$ 29.50	$ 24.50	_____	_____
The "How & Why" Book				
Spelling SOURCEBOOK™ 2	$ 29.50	$ 24.50	_____	_____
Activity Ideas for Words 1–400				
Spelling SOURCEBOOK™ Reviews	$ 39.50	$ 34.50	_____	_____
Assessments for Words 1–400				
GRADE 3				
Spelling SOURCEBOOK™ 1	$ 29.50	$ 24.50	_____	_____
The "How & Why" Book				
Spelling SOURCEBOOK™ 2	$ 29.50	$ 24.50	_____	_____
Activity Ideas for Words 1–400				
Spelling SOURCEBOOK™ Reviews	$ 39.50	$ 34.50	_____	_____
Assessments for Words 1–400				
GRADE 4				
Spelling SOURCEBOOK™ 1	$ 29.50	$ 24.50	_____	_____
The "How & Why" Book				
Spelling SOURCEBOOK™ 2	$ 29.50	$ 24.50	_____	_____
Activity Ideas for Words 1–400				
Spelling SOURCEBOOK™ Reviews	$ 39.50	$ 34.50	_____	_____
Assessments for Words 1–400				
GRADE 5				
Spelling SOURCEBOOK™ 1	$ 29.50	$ 24.50	_____	_____
The "How & Why" Book				
Spelling SOURCEBOOK™ 3	$ 29.50	$ 24.50	_____	_____
Activity Ideas for Words 401–800				
Spelling SOURCEBOOK™ Reviews	$ 39.50	$ 34.50	_____	_____
Assessments for Words 401–800				
GRADE 6				
Spelling SOURCEBOOK™ 1	$ 29.50	$ 24.50	_____	_____
The "How & Why" Book				
Spelling SOURCEBOOK™ 3	$ 29.50	$ 24.50	_____	_____
Activity Ideas for Words 401–800				
Spelling SOURCEBOOK™ Reviews	$ 39.50	$ 34.50	_____	_____
Assessments for Words 401–800				
GRADE 7				
Spelling SOURCEBOOK™ 1	$ 29.50	$ 24.50	_____	_____
The "How & Why" Book				
Spelling SOURCEBOOK™ 4	$ 29.50	$ 24.50	_____	_____
Activity Ideas for Words 801–1200				
Spelling SOURCEBOOK™ Reviews	$ 39.50	$ 34.50	_____	_____
Assessments for Words 801–1200				
GRADE 8+				
Spelling SOURCEBOOK™ 1	$ 29.50	$ 24.50	_____	_____
The "How & Why" Book				
Spelling SOURCEBOOK™ 4	$ 29.50	$ 24.50	_____	_____
Activity Ideas for Words 801–1200				
Spelling SOURCEBOOK™ Reviews	$ 39.50	$ 34.50	_____	_____
Assessments for Words 801–1200				

	PRICE	QTY. PRICE	QTY.	TOTAL
ADDITIONAL BOOKS				
Word-Wise SOURCEBOOK™ Level 1	$ 42.50	$ 37.50	_____	_____
Grades 1–2 (Wordy Birdy)				
Word-Wise SOURCEBOOK™ Level 2	$ 42.50	$ 37.50	_____	_____
Grades 3–4 (Willy Wordster)				
Word-Wise SOURCEBOOK™ Level 3	$ 42.50	$ 37.50	_____	_____
Grades 5–6 (Inspector Clue-So)				
Increasing Student Spelling Achievement				
Seminar Handbook	$ 15.00	$ 10.00		
TEACHING AIDS				
NEW My Spell Check™ K–2 (10-pack)	$ 5.50		_____	_____
With teacher resource of over 50 word activity ideas				
NEW Spell Check™ 3–8 (10-pack)	$ 5.50		_____	_____
With teacher resource of over 50 word activity ideas				
NEW! Spelling Wall Charts (set of 5)	$ 8.50		_____	_____
TRAINING VIDEOS				
Staff Development Video Series	$380.00			
Video Tape I, Introduction to Teachers				
Video Tape II, Grading and Management Options				
Video Tape III, Introduction to Parents				
Training Guide for Staff Development				
Video Tape I	$175.00		_____	_____
Video Tape II	$175.00		_____	_____
Video Tape III	$150.00		_____	_____
Training Guide	$ 30.00		_____	_____

POSTAGE AND HANDLING

	U.S.	Canada
minimum	$4.00	$8.00
$0–499	8%	14%
$500–999	$40.00	$70.00
$1000 +	4%	7%

No. Items/Subtotal _____ _____
Tax (CA 8.25%, WA 8.2%) _____
Postage/Handling _____ _____
TOTAL _____

BILL TO:

School/District: _____

Attention: _____

Address: _____

City/State/ZIP: _____

Phone: _____ FAX: _____

Purchase Order No. _____

☐ Check ☐ Visa ☐ MasterCard exp. date _____

Account No.: _____

Authorized Signature: _____

SHIP TO:

School/Attn.: _____

Address: _____

City/State/ZIP: _____

Phone: _____ FAX: _____

ALL PRICES SUBJECT TO CHANGE WITHOUT NOTICE.

WHERE TO SEND YOUR ORDER

TEXAS ONLY
Southwest Schoolbook Depository
1541 Champion Drive • Carrollton, TX 75006
800-266-5122 • FAX 972-241-4390

ALL OTHERS
Northwest Textbook Depository
P.O. Box 5608 • Portland, OR 97228
800-676-6630 • FAX 503-639-2559

Thanks for your order!
Please call Egger Publishing with any questions—888-WE-SPELL (toll free).

Every Child a Speller!

OF—0799—qxd